Scholastic Success With
1st GRADE
WORKBOOK

SCHOLASTIC
Teaching
Resources

NEW YORK • TORONTO • LONDON • AUCKLAND • SYDNEY
MEXICO CITY • NEW DELHI • HONG KONG • BUENOS AIRES

Acknowledgments

Maps workbook copyright © 2002 by Linda Ward Beech

Scholastic Inc. grants teachers permission to photocopy the reproducible pages from this book for classroom use. No other part of this publication may be reproduced in whole or in part, or stored in a retrieval system, or transmitted in any form or by any means, electronic, mechanical, photocopying, recording, or other wise without written permission of the publisher. For information regarding permission, write to Scholastic Inc., 557 Broadway, New York, NY 10012.

Cover art by Tom Ungrey and Reggie Holladay
Cover design by Rob McClurkan
Interior illustrations by Jon Buller, Reggie Holladay, Anne Kennedy,
Kathy Marlin, Bob Masheris, Sherry Neidigh, and Carol Tiernon
Interior design by Quack & Company

ISBN 978-0-545-60573-1

8 9 10 11 12   08   17 18 19 20 21

Table of Contents

Scholastic Professional Books

Scholastic Professional Books

"Nothing succeeds like success."

Alexandre Dumas the Elder, 1854

Dear Parent,

Congratulations on choosing this excellent educational resource for your child. Scholastic has long been a leader in educational publishing—creating quality educational materials for use in school and at home for nearly a century.

As a partner in your child's academic success, you'll want to get the most out of the learning experience offered in this book. To help your child learn at home, try following these helpful hints:

- Provide a comfortable place to work.

- Have frequent work sessions, but keep them short.

- Praise your child's successes and encourage his or her efforts. Offer positive help when a child makes a mistake.

- Display your child's work and share his or her progress with family and friends.

In this workbook you'll find hundreds of practice pages that keep kids challenged and excited as they strengthen their skills across the classroom curriculum.

The workbook is divided into eight sections: Reading Comprehension; Reading Tests; Traditional Manuscript; Grammar; Writing; Maps; Addition & Subtraction; and Math. You and your child should feel free to move through the pages in any way you wish.

The table of contents lists the activities and the skills practiced. And a complete answer key in the back will help you gauge your child's progress.

Take the lead and help your child succeed with the *Scholastic Success With: 1st Grade Workbook!*

The activities in this workbook reinforce age-appropriate skills and will help your child meet the following standards established as goals by leading educators.

Mathematics

★ Uses a variety of strategies when problem-solving

★ Understands and applies number concepts

★ Uses basic and advanced procedures while performing computation

★ Understands and applies concepts of measurement

★ Understands and applies concepts of geometry

Writing

★ Understands and uses the writing process

★ Uses grammatical and mechanical conventions in written compositions

Reading

★ Understands and uses the general skills and strategies of the reading process

★ Can read and understand a variety of literary texts

★ Can understand and interpret a variety of informational texts

Geography

★ Understands the characteristics and uses of maps and globes

★ Knows the location of places, geographic features, and patterns of the environment

Ricky's Wish

➤ **Details** *are parts of a story. Details help you understand what the story is about.*

Ricky loved to go camping. One day during reading class, he began to daydream about camping in the mountains. He thought about going fishing and riding horses. It would be fun to gather logs to build a campfire and cook hot dogs. He and his dad could set up the tent near some big trees. He wished he were in his canoe right now. Just then, Ricky heard his teacher say, "Ricky, it is your turn to read." Oh no! He had lost the place!

Circle these things from the story hidden in the picture below: a fish, a fishing pole, a log for the campfire, a hot dog, a tree, and a canoe.

1. Where was Ricky during this story? _____

_____

2. Where would Ricky like to have been? _____

_____

💡 **What do you like to daydream about? Write about it using details.**

Going to Grammy's

Kelly is going to spend the night with her grandmother. She will need to take her pajamas, a shirt, and some shorts. Into the suitcase go her toothbrush, toothpaste, and hairbrush. Grammy told her to bring a swimsuit in case it was warm enough to swim. Mom said to pack her favorite pillow and storybooks. Dad said, "Don't forget to take Grammy's sunglasses that she left here last week." Now Kelly is ready to go!

1. Color the things that Kelly packed in her suitcase.

2. A compound word is a big word that is made up of two little words. For example, cow + boy = cowboy. Find 8 compound words in this story and circle them.

On the back of this page, make a list of things you would pack if you were going to spend the night at your grandmother's house.

Scholastic Professional Books

George W. Bush

George W. Bush grew up in Texas. When he finished college, he worked in the oil business. Later on, he became the governor of Texas, then the 43rd president of the United States. His wife's name is Laura. They have twin daughters named Jenna and Barbara. The Bush family owns a ranch in Texas. They had two dogs named Barney and Spotty.

The Bush family also had a cat. To find out the name of their cat, write the answers in the blanks. Then copy the letters that are in the shapes into the empty shapes below.

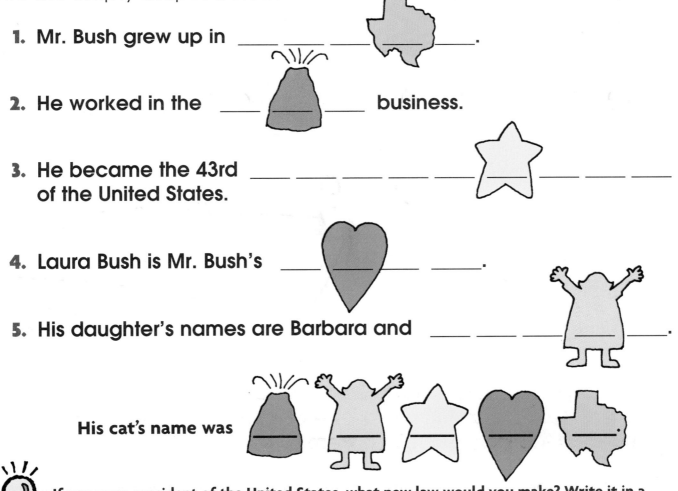

1. Mr. Bush grew up in _____ _____.

2. He worked in the _____ business.

3. He became the 43rd _____ _____ of the United States.

4. Laura Bush is Mr. Bush's _____ _____.

5. His daughter's names are Barbara and _____.

His cat's name was _____

 If you were president of the United States, what new law would you make? Write it in a complete sentence, including three details.

Mr. Lee's Store

 *Story events that can really happen are **real**. Story events that are make-believe are **fantasy**.*

At night, Mr. Lee locked the store and went home. That's when the fun began! The ketchup bottles stood in rows like bowling pins. Then the watermelon rolled down the aisle and knocked them down. The chicken wings flew around the room. Cans of soup stacked themselves higher and higher until they laughed so hard that they tumbled over. Carrots danced with bananas. Then it was morning. "Get back in your places!" called the milk jug. "Mr. Lee is coming!" Mr. Lee opened the door and went right to work.

Circle the cans that are make-believe.

ketchup bottles and a watermelon bowling

a talking milk jug

dancing bananas

chicken wings that can fly all by themselves

Mr. Lee went to work.

laughing soup cans

Mr. Lee went home at night.

dancing carrots

a grocery store

Draw a picture of the story on another piece of paper.

Cool Clouds

Have you ever looked up in the sky and seen a cloud that is shaped like an animal or a person? Big, white, puffy clouds float along like soft marshmallows. In cartoons, people can sit on clouds and bounce on them. But clouds are really just tiny drops of water floating in the air. You can understand what being in a cloud is like when it is foggy. Fog is a cloud on the ground!

Read each sentence below. If the sentence could really happen, color the cloud blue. If the sentence is make-believe, color it orange.

Clouds float in the sky.

A cartoon dog sleeps on a cloud.

Clouds are made of tiny drops of water.

Animal shapes in clouds are made by the Cloud Fairy.

Clouds are big blobs of whipped cream.

Clouds are made of marshmallows.

Fog is a cloud on the ground.

Birds can hop around on clouds.

Draw a picture to show a real cloud. Then draw a make-believe cloud.

Fun at the Farm

 Story events that can really happen are **real**. *Story events that are make-believe are* **fantasy**.

Read each sentence below. If it could be real, circle the picture. If it is make-believe, put an X on the picture.

 Dairy cows give milk.

 The farmer planted pizza and hamburgers.

 The pig said,"Let's go to the dance tonight!"

 The mouse ate the dinner table.

 The hay was stacked in the barn.

 The chickens laid golden eggs.

 The green tractor ran out of gas.

 The newborn calf walked with wobbly legs.

 The goat and the sheep got married by the big tree.

 Two crickets sang "Mary Had a Little Lamb."

 Horses sat on the couch and watched TV.

 Rain made the roads muddy.

Four little ducks swam in the pond.

The farmer's wife baked a pumpkin pie.

💡 **On another sheet of paper, write one make-believe sentence about the farmer's house and one real sentence about it.**

Scholastic Professional Books

Ready for School

Sequencing *means putting the events in a story in the order they happened.*

Tara could hardly wait for school to start. Mom drove her to the store to buy school supplies. They bought pencils, crayons, scissors, and glue. When Tara got home, she wrote her name on all of her supplies. She put them in a paper sack. The next day, Tara went to school, but the principal told her and the other children to go back home. A water leak had flooded the building. Oh no! Tara would have to wait another whole week!

Number the pictures in the order that they happened in the story.

Color the supplies that Tara bought.

Scholastic Professional Books

Swimming Lessons

Sequencing *means putting the events in a story in the order they happened.*

Last summer I learned how to swim. First, the teacher told me to hold my breath. Then I learned to put my head under water. I practiced kicking my feet. While I held on to a float, I paddled around the pool. Next, I floated to my teacher with my arms straight out. Finally, I swam using both my arms and my legs. I did it! Swimming is fun! This summer, I want to learn to dive off the diving board.

Number the pictures in the order that they happened in the story.

Unscramble the letters to tell what the person in the story wants to do next.

EALNR   **OT**   **IVDE**

____ ____ ____ ____ ____   ____ ____   ____ ____ ____ ____

What would you like to learn to do? Draw four pictures on the back of your paper to show how to do it.

Shapes in the Sky

Be sure to read directions carefully.

Follow the directions.

1. Outline each star with a blue crayon. Then color each one red.

2. Color one moon yellow. Color the other one orange.

3. Draw a face on every sun.

4. Write the number of stars inside the star.

5. Write the number of moons inside the moon.

6. Write the number of suns inside the sun.

7. Add the three numbers you wrote together to find the total number of shapes.

   _____ + _____ + _____ = _____

8. Which two shapes belong in the night sky?

   _____ and _____

My Monster

Be sure to read directions carefully. Look for key words like circle, underline, *and* color.

I saw a scary monster who lived in a cave. He had shaggy fur and a long, striped tail. He had ugly, black teeth. His three horns were shaped like arrows. His nose was crooked. One of his feet was bigger than the other three. "Wake up! Time for breakfast," Mom said. Oh, good! It was only a dream.

Follow the directions.

1. What did the monster's tail look like? Circle it.

2. What did the monster's teeth look like? Draw a box around them.

3. What did the monster's horns look like? Color them green.

4. What did the monster's nose look like? Underline it.

5. What did the monster's feet look like? Color them red.

6. Which one of these is the correct picture of the monster? Draw a cave around him.

Fun at the Beach

Jack and Joni went to the beach today. Mom spread a blanket on the sand, and they had a picnic. It got very hot, so Jack and Joni jumped into the cold water. They climbed onto a big yellow raft. The waves made the raft go up and down. Later, they played in the sand and built sandcastles. Jack and Joni picked up pretty shells. Joni found a starfish. What a fun day!

1. Color the pictures below that are from the story. Put an X on the ones that don't belong.

2. In the third sentence, find two words that are opposites of each other and circle them with a red crayon.

3. In the fifth sentence, find two more words that are opposites of each other and circle them with a blue crayon.

4. Draw a box around the compound word that tells what Joni found.

5. What color was the raft? Show your answer by coloring the picture at the top of the page.

Write three sentences that tell how to get ready to play your favorite sport.

My New Rug

When you use your own thoughts to answer the question, "How could that have happened?", you are **drawing conclusions**.

I bought a fancy rug today. It was made of brightly-colored yarn. I placed it on the floor in front of the TV and sat on it. All of a sudden, it lifted me up in the air! The rug and I flew around the house. Then out the door we went. High above the trees, we soared like an eagle. Finally, it took me home, and we landed in my backyard.

How could that have happened? To find out, use your crayons to trace over each line. Use a different color on each line. Write the letter from that line in the box at the bottom of the rug.

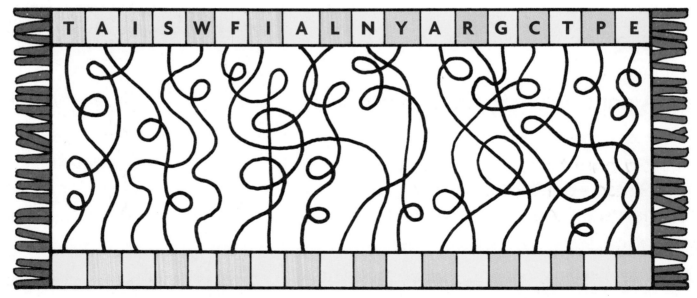

Could this story really happen? Draw a rug around your answer.

Yes   **No**

You left your ball on the steps. Your mother came down the steps carrying the laundry basket. Draw a picture of what you think happened.

Scholastic Professional Books

Polly Want a Cracker?

Have you ever heard a parrot talk? Parrots are able to copy sounds that they hear. You can train a parrot to repeat words, songs, and whistles. But a parrot cannot say words that it has never heard. People can use words to make new sentences, but most parrots cannot.

Read each sentence. If it is true, color the parrot under True.
If it is false, color the parrot under False.

True   **False**

1. You could teach a parrot to sing "Happy Birthday."

2. You could ask a parrot any question, and it could give the answer.

3. A parrot could make up a fairy tale.

4. If a parrot heard your mom say, "Brush your teeth," every night, he could learn to say it, too.

5. It is possible for a parrot to repeat words in Spanish.

Write what would happen if a parrot heard you say, "No, I can't" too often.

You Be the Artist

Picturing a story can help the reader understand it better.

An artist drew the pictures that are in this book. Now it is your turn to be the artist! Read each sentence very carefully. Draw exactly what you read about in the sentence.

1. **The green and yellow striped snake wiggled past the ants.**

2. **Wildflowers grew along the banks of the winding river.**

3. **On her sixth birthday, Shannon had a pink birthday cake shaped like a butterfly.**

Now write your own sentence and illustrate it.

Scholastic Professional Books

A Stormy Day

Big, black clouds appeared in the sky. Lightning struck the tallest tree. The scared cow cried, "Moo!" It rained hard. Soon there was a mud puddle by the barn door. Hay blew out of the barn window.

Read the story above. Then go back and read each sentence again. Add to the picture everything that the sentences describe.

Who Am I?

 Use details from the story to make decisions about the characters.

Circle the picture that answers the riddle.

1. I have feathers. I also have wings, but I don't fly. I love to swim in icy water. Who am I?

2. I am 3 weeks old. I drink milk. I cry when my diaper is wet. Who am I?

3. I live in the ocean. I swim around slowly, looking for something to eat. I have six more arms than you have. Who am I?

4. I am an insect. If you touch me, I might bite you! I make tunnels under the ground. I love to come to your picnic! Who am I?

5. I am a female. I like to watch movies and listen to music. My grandchildren love my oatmeal cookies. Who am I?

6. I am a large mammal. I live in the woods. I have fur. I stand up and growl when I am angry. Who am I?

7. I wear a uniform. My job is to help people. I ride on a big red truck. Who am I?

💡 **Write your own riddle and let the class guess the answer.**

My Favorites

This page is all about you! Read the categories and write your own answers.

My Favorite TV Shows	My Favorite Foods	My Favorite Sports
_____	_____	_____
_____	_____	_____
_____	_____	_____

Draw two of your favorite people here and write their names.

Favorite Color

_____

Favorite Holiday

_____

Favorite Song

_____

Favorite Thing to Do After School

_____

Favorite Movie

_____

Favorite Thing to Do With My Family

_____

Favorite School Subject

_____

Trade pages with friends and read what they wrote. You might get to know them a little better!

Ouch!

Use story details to make a guess of what will happen next.

Mia and Rosa were playing hospital. Mia was the patient, and Rosa was the doctor. Rosa pretended to take Mia's temperature. "You have a fever," she said. "You will have to lie down." Mia climbed onto the top bunk bed. "You need to sleep," Dr. Rosa said. Mia rolled over too far and fell off the top bunk. "O-o-o-h, my arm!" yelled Mia. Her mother came to look. It was broken!

What do you think happened next? Write your answer here.

a real hospital

To find out if your answer is correct, finish the sentence below by coloring only the spaces that have a dot in them.

Mia had to go to

If Mia hadn't fallen off the bed, how do you think this story would have ended? Draw your answer.

What Will Sam Do?

One day, Sam was riding his bike to the baseball game. He had to be on time. He was the pitcher. Just ahead, Sam saw a little boy who had fallen off his bike. His knee was bleeding, and he was crying. Sam asked him if he was okay, but the boy couldn't speak English. Sam knew the boy needed help getting home. If he stopped to help, he might be late for the game. Sam thought about it. He knew he had to do the right thing.

What do you think Sam did next? There are two paths through the maze. Draw a line down the path that shows what you think Sam did next.

What sentence from the story gives you a hint about what Sam decided to do? Write that sentence below.

 The maze shows two ways the story could end. Draw a different ending to the story and tell about your picture.

Riddle Fun

 Compare *means to look for things that are the same.*
Contrast *means to look for things that are different.*

To solve the riddles in each box, read the clues in the horse.
Then write the letters in the blanks with the matching numbers.

What kind of food does a racehorse like to eat?

___ ___ ___ ___   ___ ___ ___ ___
11   5   10   3   11   9   9   2

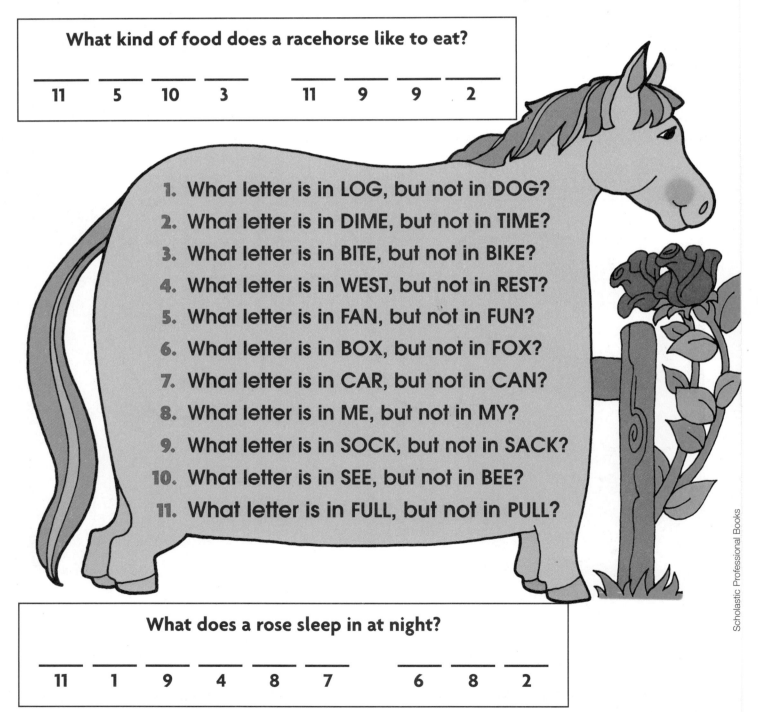

1. What letter is in LOG, but not in DOG?
2. What letter is in DIME, but not in TIME?
3. What letter is in BITE, but not in BIKE?
4. What letter is in WEST, but not in REST?
5. What letter is in FAN, but not in FUN?
6. What letter is in BOX, but not in FOX?
7. What letter is in CAR, but not in CAN?
8. What letter is in ME, but not in MY?
9. What letter is in SOCK, but not in SACK?
10. What letter is in SEE, but not in BEE?
11. What letter is in FULL, but not in PULL?

What does a rose sleep in at night?

___ ___ ___ ___ ___ ___   ___ ___ ___
11   1   9   4   8   7   6   8   2

Dinosaur Clues

How do we know that dinosaurs were real? It is because their bones have been found in rocks. Sometimes scientists have found dinosaur footprints where mud later turned to stone. These kinds of rocks are called fossils. Fossils give us clues about how big the dinosaurs were. Some were small and some were very large. Scientists say a diplodocus was as big as three school buses!

1. Color the picture that shows scientists working.

2. Color the picture of a fossil.

3. Color the picture of a diplodocus.

Find and write the names of three more dinosaurs.

Amazing Animal Facts

Read each sentence. Then color the picture that tells the meaning of the underlined word.

1. Sea lions sometimes sleep in the water with one <u>flipper</u> up in the air.

an arm like a paddle   a beak   a feather

2. Even though whale sharks are the biggest fish in the world, they are <u>harmless</u> to people.

reddish brown   not dangerous   very tiny

3. Horses use their tails to <u>swat</u> pesky flies.

slap at   catch   eat

4. Snakes <u>shed</u> their old skins and grow new ones.

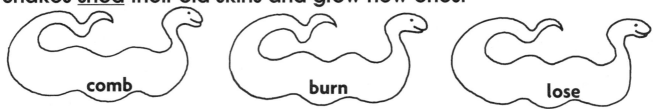

comb   burn   lose

5. Squirrels <u>bury</u> acorns and nuts to eat when winter comes.

bake   hide in the ground   steal

 Write an interesting fact about two other animals.

Scholastic Professional Books

A Tiny Town

Have you ever seen a prairie dog
town? That's where prairie dogs live,
but there are no buildings or houses.
They live underground. They dig deep
into the dirt making burrows. Along the
burrows, here and there, are chambers for sleeping or storing
food. One chamber is lined with grass for the babies. Sometimes
prairie dogs have unwanted guests in their town, like rattlesnakes!

Use the code below to learn what some of the words in the story
mean. Copy the matching letters in the blanks.

Oops!

In a story, there is usually a reason something happens.
This is the **cause**. What happens as a result is the **effect**.

Sandy went on a vacation in the mountains
with her parents and little brother Austin. They were
staying in a small cabin without any electricity or
running water. It was fun to have lanterns at night
and to bathe in the cold mountain stream. The
biggest problem for Sandy was she missed her
best friend, Kendra. Sandy found her dad's cell
phone and called Kendra. They talked for nearly
an hour! When Sandy's dad went to call his office,
the cell phone was dead. He was NOT a happy camper!

Draw a line to match the first part of each sentence to the second
part that makes it true.

1. **Sandy used lanterns
   at night because**

2. **Sandy and Austin
   bathed in a stream
   because**

3. **Sandy felt better
   about missing
   Kendra because**

4. **Sandy's dad could
   not call his office
   because**

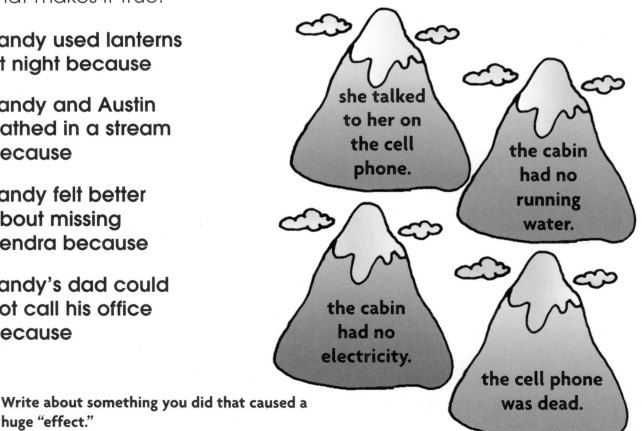

she talked
to her on
the cell
phone.

the cabin
had no
running
water.

the cabin
had no
electricity.

the cell phone
was dead.

**Write about something you did that caused a
huge "effect."**

Scholastic Professional Books

Wanda Wiggleworm

*In a story, there is usually a reason something happens.
This is the **cause**. What happens as a result is the **effect**.*

Wanda Wiggleworm was tired of
living alone in the flowerpot, so she
decided to live it up. Last night, Wanda
went to the Ugly Bug Ball. She looked her
best, all slick and slimy. Carl Caterpillar
asked her to dance. They twisted and
wiggled around and around to the
music. All of a sudden, they got tangled up. They tried to get free,
but instead, they tied themselves in a knot! What would they do?
They decided to get married, and they lived happily ever after.

Unscramble each sentence about the story.
Write the new sentence on the line.

| tangled | worms | when | got | danced. | they | The | up |

_____

_____

| in | knot | They | married. | a | they | were | so | got | tied |

_____

_____

Tim fell asleep on his raft while playing in the lake. Draw a picture of what you think the
effect was on Tim.

School Rules

It is important to follow the rules at school. Read each rule below. Find the picture that shows what would happen if students DID NOT follow that rule. Write the letter of the picture in the correct box.

1. You must walk, not run, in the halls. ☐

2. Do not chew gum at school. ☐

3. Come to school on time. ☐

4. When the fire alarm rings, follow the leader outside. ☐

5. Listen when the teacher is talking. ☐

6. Keep your desk clean. ☐

Write a school rule that you must obey. Draw a picture of what might happen if you do not.

Mixed-Up Margie

 A character is a person or animal in a story. To help readers understand a character better, a story often gives details about the character.

Once upon a time there was a mixed-up queen named Margie. She got things mixed up. She wore her crown on her arm. She wore a shoe on her head. She painted every fingernail a different color. Then she painted her nose red! She used a fork to hold her hair in place. She wore a purple belt around her knees. The king didn't mind. He always wore his clothes backward!

Use the story and your crayons to help you follow these instructions:

1. Draw Margie's crown.

2. Draw her shoe.

3. Paint her fingernails and nose.

4. Draw what goes in her hair.

5. Draw her belt.

Circle the correct answer:

6. What makes you think Margie is mixed up?

   the way she dresses

   the way she talks

7. What makes you think the king is mixed up, too?

   He talks backward.

   He wears his clothes backward.

 Pretend tomorrow is Mixed-Up Day. Describe what you will wear as a mixed-up character.

Scholastic Professional Books

Miss Ticklefoot

I love Miss Ticklefoot. She is my first-grade teacher.

To find out more about her, read each sentence below. Write a word in each blank that tells how she feels. The Word Box will help you.

Word Box

| sad | scared | silly | worried | happy | surprised |

1. **Miss Ticklefoot smiles when we know the answers.**

   _____

2. **She is concerned when one of us is sick.**

   _____

3. **She makes funny faces at us during recess.**

   _____

4. **She cried when our fish died.**

   _____

5. **She jumps when the fire alarm rings.**

   _____

6. **Her mouth dropped open when we gave her a present!**

   _____

Different Friends

When Ty was four years old, he had two make-believe friends named Mr. Go-Go and Mr. Sasso. They lived in Ty's closet. When there was no one else around, Ty talked to Mr. Go-Go while he played with his toys. Mr. Go-Go was a good friend. He helped put Ty's toys away. Mr. Sasso was not a good friend. Some days he forgot to make Ty's bed or brush Ty's teeth. One day he even talked back to Ty's mother. Another day Dad said, "Oh my! Who wrote on the wall?" Ty knew who did it . . . Mr. Sasso!

Read the phrase inside each crayon. If it describes Mr. Go-Go, color it green. If it describes Mr. Sasso, color it red. If it describes both, color it yellow.

1. helpful

2. probably sassy

3. forgets to do chores

4. friends that live in the closet

5. could get Ty in trouble

6. make-believe characters

7. does the right thing

Draw Mr. Go-Go.

Draw Mr. Sasso.

Write something you think Mr. Sasso and Mr. Go-Go might do.

Poetry

A poem paints a picture with words. It often uses rhyming words.

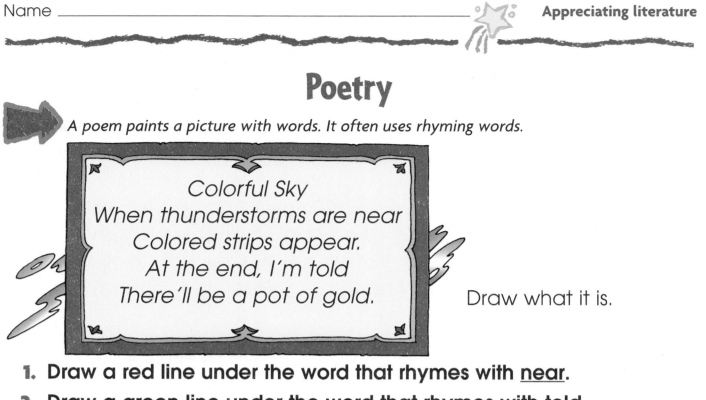

Colorful Sky
When thunderstorms are near
Colored strips appear.
At the end, I'm told
There'll be a pot of gold.

Draw what it is.

1. **Draw a red line under the word that rhymes with <u>near</u>.**

2. **Draw a green line under the word that rhymes with <u>told</u>.**

What's That in the Sky?
It flies up in the sky.
It takes you way up high.
You see an airport, then
It takes you down again.

Draw what it is.

3. **Draw a blue circle around the word that rhymes with <u>sky</u>.**

4. **Draw a brown circle around the word that rhymes with <u>then</u>.**

5. **Finish this two-line poem:**

         I wish that I could see

         A giant bumble_____.

Draw what it is.

Now see if you can make up your own two-line poem using these rhyming words at the end of each line: G0 and SNOW.

Scholastic Professional Books

A Fable

 A fable is a story that teaches a lesson. This fable was written many, many years ago.

The Dog and His Shadow

A dog carried a piece of meat in his mouth. He crossed over a river on a low bridge. He looked down into the water and saw his reflection. It looked like another dog with a piece of meat larger than his. The dog snapped at the other dog's meat. When he did, his own meat dropped into the water. Now the dog didn't have any meat at all.

Draw a box around the lesson that the story teaches:

1. Two dogs are better than one.

2. Don't be greedy. Be happy with what you have.

Color only the pictures of things that you read about in the story:

Write a complete sentence telling what the dog should have done.

Library Books

A library has many different kinds of books.

It is fun to check books out of the library. Have you ever read *The Rainbow Fish* by Marcus Pfister? It is a story about a very special fish. His scales were blue, green, and purple. He also had some shiny, silver scales. The other fish wanted him to share his shiny scales with them, but he said no. No one would be his friend. Later, he decided to give each fish one of his shiny scales. It was better to lose some of his beauty and have friends than to keep them to himself.

Connect the dots. You will see something from the book.

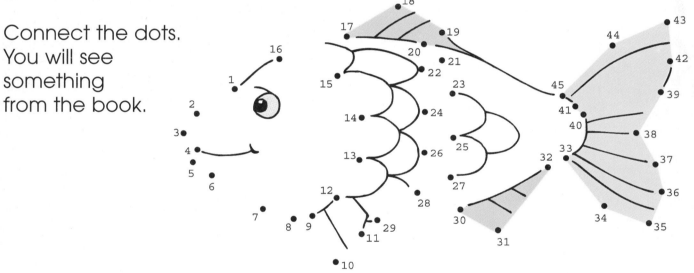

1. Draw a blue circle around the word that tells what this book is about:

running   lying   sharing   eating

2. Copy the name of the author here.

_____

- -

_____

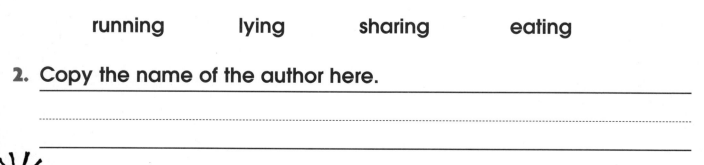

If you grew up to be an author, what would you write about? Make a pretty book cover that includes the title of your book.

Scholastic Professional Books

Scholastic Success With

TESTS: READING

Reading Skills Practice Test 1

A. Phonic Analysis: Consonants and Vowels
Look at each picture.
Write the missing letter on the blank line.

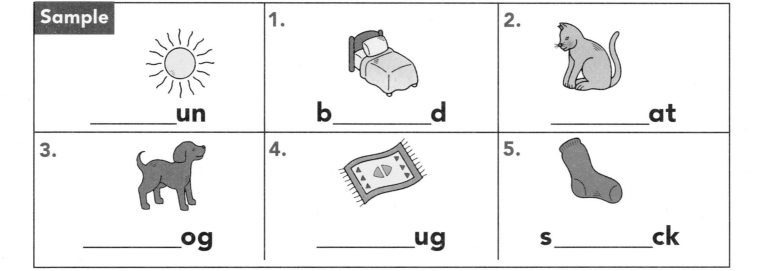

Sample	**1.**	**2.**
_____un	b_____d	_____at
3.	**4.**	**5.**
_____og	_____ug	s_____ck

B. Vocabulary: Picture-Word Match
Circle the word that names each picture.

Sample	**1.**	**2.**	**3.**
cat	dig	run	car
can	pet	bun	rock
cot	pig	rat	lick

Scholastic Professional Books

C. High-frequency Word Match

Circle the word your teacher says out loud.

Sample	1.	2.	3.
the of and	are my like	will who he	his sad has

D. Grammar, Usage, and Mechanics

Each sentence has a mistake.
Write each sentence correctly on the blank line.

Sample My bike is red

_____

- -

_____

1. i like to run.

_____

- -

_____

2. Did you see it

_____

- -

_____

3. They sits on the mat.

_____

- -

_____

Scholastic Professional Books

E. Reading Sentences

Fill in the bubble next to the sentence that tells about each picture.

Sample		○ A girl sits. ○ A girl walks. ○ A girl runs.
1.		○ The boy plays ball. ○ The cat plays. ○ The girls run and play.
2.		○ The book is on the desk. ○ He has two books. ○ The pen is next to the book.
3.		○ We have a big bag. ○ She has a rabbit. ○ He has a rug and a pan.
4.		○ Six pigs sit. ○ The dog sits on a hill. ○ A pig plays in the mud.

F. Story Comprehension
Read the story. Then answer each question.
Fill in the bubble next to the best answer.

> **Pam has a dog. His name is Rags.**
>
> **Rags likes to play.**
>
> **Rags likes to run.**
>
> **Rags likes to jump.**
>
> **Rags is a good dog!**

1. What kind of pet does Pam have?
- ○ cat
- ○ dog
- ○ rabbit

2. What is a good title (name) for this story?
- ○ Rags the Dog
- ○ Frogs Jump
- ○ Apples Grow on Trees

3. What does Rags like to do?
- ○ skip
- ○ play
- ○ sing

Scholastic Professional Books

Reading Skills Practice Test 2

A. Phonic Analysis: Consonants

Look at each picture.
Write the missing letter on the line.

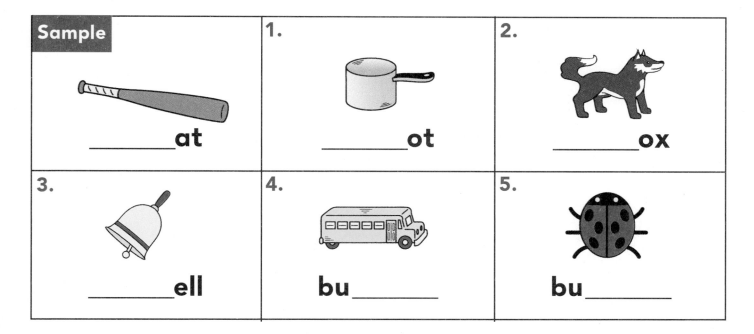

Sample
_____at

1.
_____ot

2.
_____ox

3.
_____ell

4.
bu_____

5.
bu_____

B. Phonic Analysis: Vowels

Look at each picture.
Write the missing letter on the line.

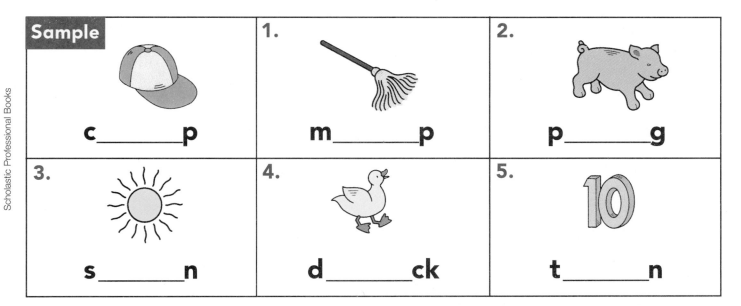

Sample
c_____p

1.
m_____p

2.
p_____g

3.
s_____n

4.
d_____ck

5.
t_____n

C. High-Frequency Word Match
Circle the word your teacher says out loud.

Sample	1.	2.	3.	4.	5.
to	my	she	who	this	then
of	it	he	has	at	they
and	like	saw	was	that	thing

D. Vocabulary: Picture-Word Match
Fill in the bubble next to the word that names each picture.

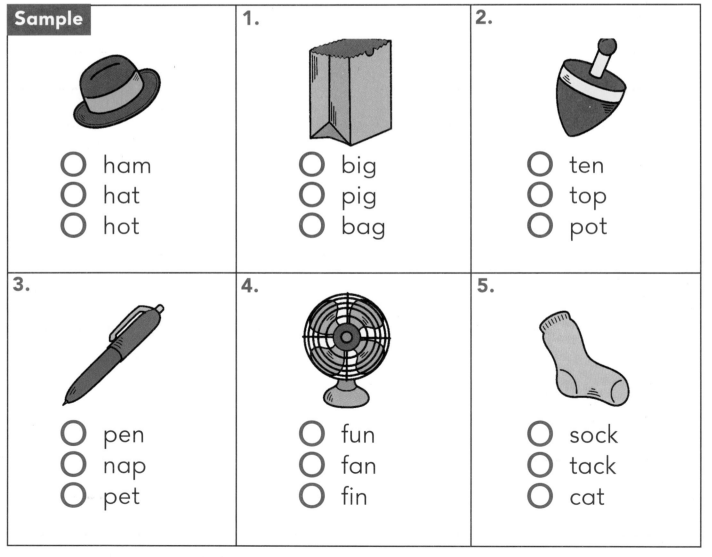

Sample
- ○ ham
- ○ hat
- ○ hot

1.
- ○ big
- ○ pig
- ○ bag

2.
- ○ ten
- ○ top
- ○ pot

3.
- ○ pen
- ○ nap
- ○ pet

4.
- ○ fun
- ○ fan
- ○ fin

5.
- ○ sock
- ○ tack
- ○ cat

E. Grammar, Usage, and Mechanics

Each sentence has a mistake.
Write each sentence correctly on the blank line.

Sample   the boy is happy.

_____

- -

_____

1. She saw a duck

_____

- -

_____

2. look at him run!

_____

- -

_____

3. Where will i go?

_____

- -

_____

F. Story Comprehension

Read the story. Then answer each question.
Fill in the bubble next to the best answer.

> **Ted has a pig.**
>
> **The pig's name is Big.**
>
> **Big lives in a pen.**
>
> **He plays in the mud.**
>
> **Big is a very big pig!**

1. What does Ted have?
  O a dog
  O a pig
  O a cat

2. What is a good title (name) for this story?
  O Ted's Pig
  O Sam's Pig
  O Pig Pens

3. Write a sentence telling something about Big the Pig.

_____

- -

_____

_____

- -

_____

Scholastic Professional Books

Reading Skills Practice Test 3

A. Phonic Analysis: Consonants
Look at each picture.
Write the missing letter or letters on the line.

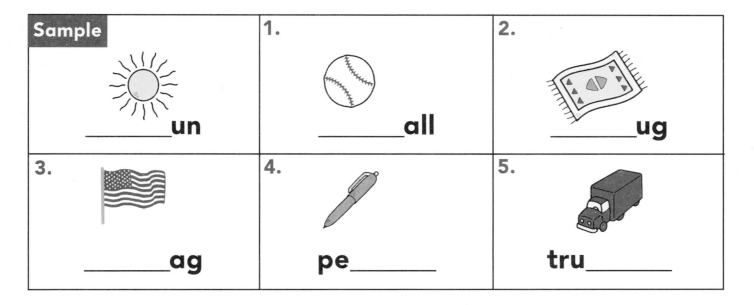

Sample	1.	2.
_____un	_____all	_____ug
3.	**4.**	**5.**
_____ag	pe_____	tru_____

B. Phonic Analysis: Vowels
Look at each picture.
Write the missing letter or letters on the line.

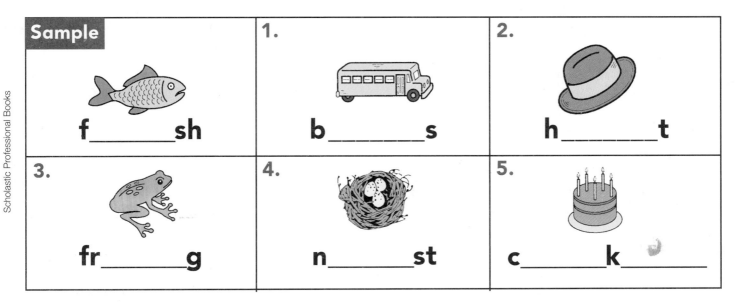

Sample	1.	2.
f_____sh	b_____s	h_____t
3.	**4.**	**5.**
fr_____g	n_____st	c_____k_____

Scholastic Professional Books

C. High-Frequency Word Match

Circle the word your teacher says out loud.

Sample	1.	2.	3.	4.	5.
and	for	she	who	so	them
is	but	see	you	could	time
with	have	he	out	said	these

D. Vocabulary: Picture-Word Match

Fill in the bubble next to the word that names each picture.

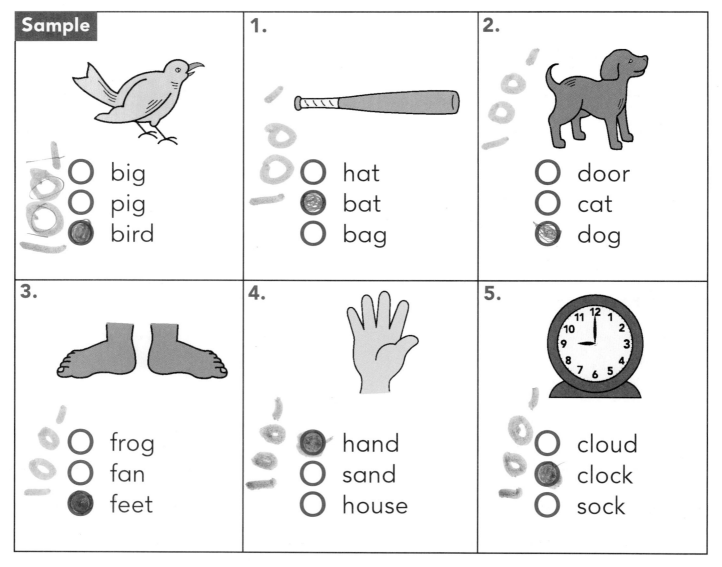

Sample
- ○ big
- ○ pig
- ● bird

1.
- ○ hat
- ● bat
- ○ bag

2.
- ○ door
- ○ cat
- ● dog

3.
- ○ frog
- ○ fan
- ● feet

4.
- ● hand
- ○ sand
- ○ house

5.
- ○ cloud
- ● clock
- ○ sock

Scholastic Professional Books

E. Grammar, Usage, and Mechanics

Each sentence has a mistake.
Write each sentence correctly on the line.

Sample   the girl can jump.

The girl can jump.

1. The boy ran fast

The boy ran fast.

2. look at me!

Look at me!

3. Where will i walk?

Where will I walk?

F. Story Comprehension

Read the story. Then answer each question.
Fill in the bubble next to the best answer.

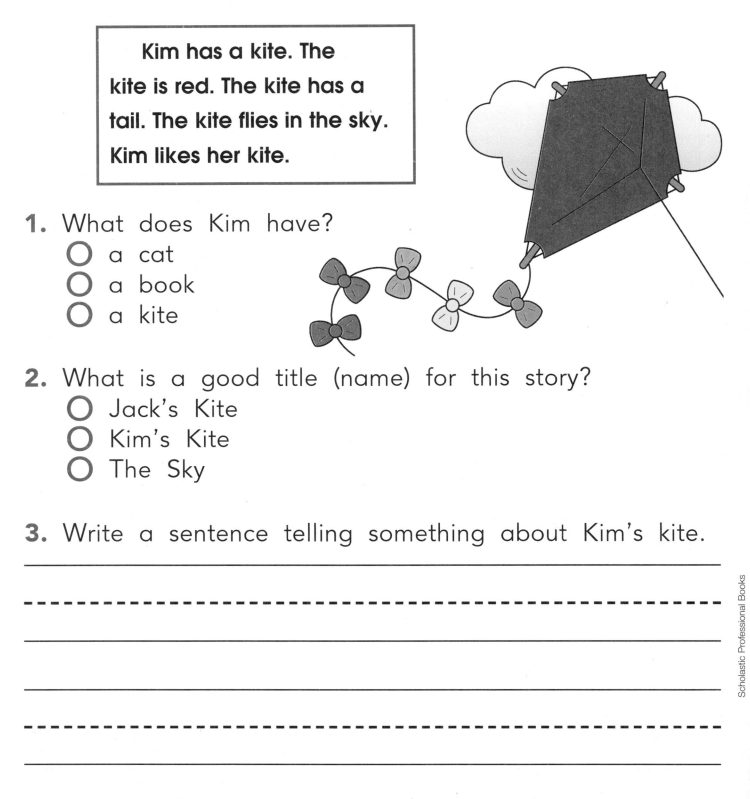

> Kim has a kite. The
> kite is red. The kite has a
> tail. The kite flies in the sky.
> Kim likes her kite.

1. What does Kim have?
- ○ a cat
- ○ a book
- ○ a kite

2. What is a good title (name) for this story?
- ○ Jack's Kite
- ○ Kim's Kite
- ○ The Sky

3. Write a sentence telling something about Kim's kite.

_____

_____

_____

_____

Reading Skills Practice Test 4

A. Phonic Analysis: Consonants
Look at each picture.
Write the missing letter or letters on the line.

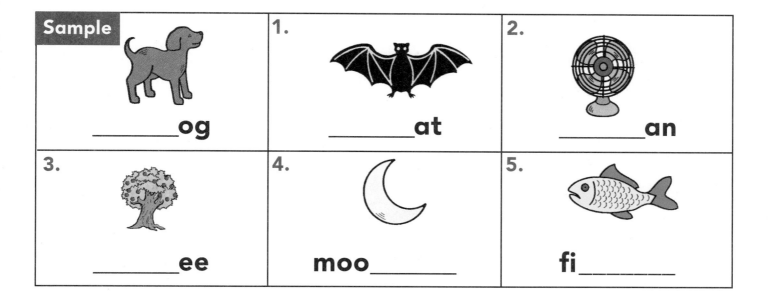

Sample	1.	2.
_____og	_____at	_____an
3.	4.	5.
_____ee	moo_____	fi_____

B. Phonic Analysis: Vowels
Look at each picture.
Write the missing letter or letters on the line.

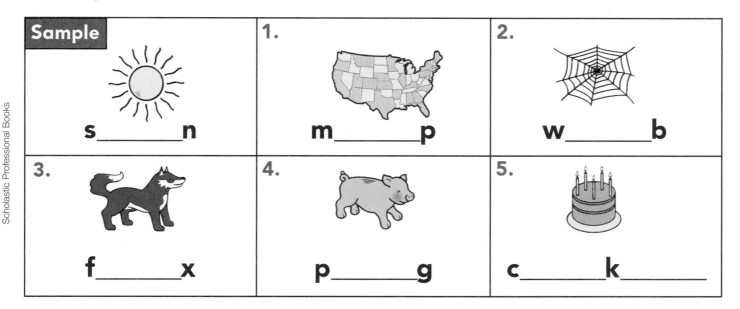

Sample	1.	2.
s_____n	m_____p	w_____b
3.	4.	5.
f_____x	p_____g	c_____k_____

Scholastic Professional Books

C. High-Frequency Word Match
Circle the word your teacher says out loud.

Sample	1.	2.	3.	4.	5.
and	from	she	who	can	this
at	for	see	you	could	ten
all	or	say	how	should	then

D. Vocabulary: Picture-Word Match
Fill in the bubble next to the word that names each picture.

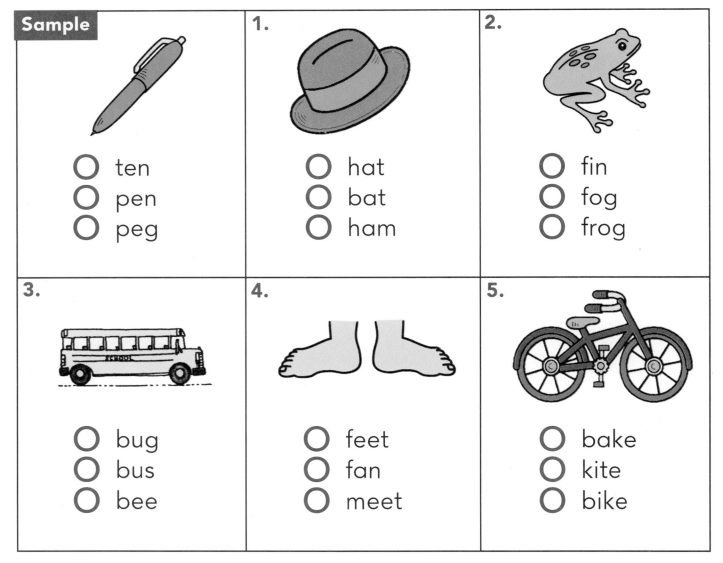

Sample	1.	2.
O ten O pen O peg	O hat O bat O ham	O fin O fog O frog

3.	4.	5.
O bug O bus O bee	O feet O fan O meet	O bake O kite O bike

Scholastic Professional Books

E. Grammar, Usage, and Mechanics

Read each sentence. Fill in the bubble next to the word or words that best complete each sentence.

Sample

_____ boy can sing.
- ⃝ the
- ⃝ The
- ⃝ he

1. _____ likes to swim.
- ⃝ She
- ⃝ she
- ⃝ the

2. _____ ride a bus.
- ⃝ they
- ⃝ They
- ⃝ she

3. Look _____
- ⃝ out?
- ⃝ out.
- ⃝ out!

4. How was your _____
- ⃝ day!
- ⃝ day?
- ⃝ day.

5. Her name is _____
- ⃝ Amy.
- ⃝ amy.
- ⃝ jen.

6. That's what ____ said.
- ⃝ He
- ⃝ I
- ⃝ i

7. _____ walk to school.
- ⃝ She
- ⃝ We
- ⃝ He

8. What is _____ name?
- ⃝ he
- ⃝ his
- ⃝ him

9. ____ work on a puzzle.
- ⃝ anna and tim
- ⃝ Anna and Tim
- ⃝ Anna

F. Story Comprehension

Read the story. Then answer each question.
Fill in the bubble next to the best answer.

> Nate has a cat. The cat's name is
> Sam. Sam is gray. Sam likes to play
> with string. Nate loves his cat!

1. What does Nate have?
- ○ a cap
- ○ a cat
- ○ a dog

2. What does Sam like to play with?
- ○ string
- ○ cats
- ○ hats

3. What is a good title for this story?
- ○ Sam's Cat
- ○ Nate's String
- ○ Nate's Cat

4. Write a sentence telling something about Nate's cat.

_____

- -

_____

_____

- -

Scholastic Professional Books

Reading Skills Practice Test 6

A. Phonic Analysis: Consonants

Look at each picture.
Write the missing letter or letters on the blank line.

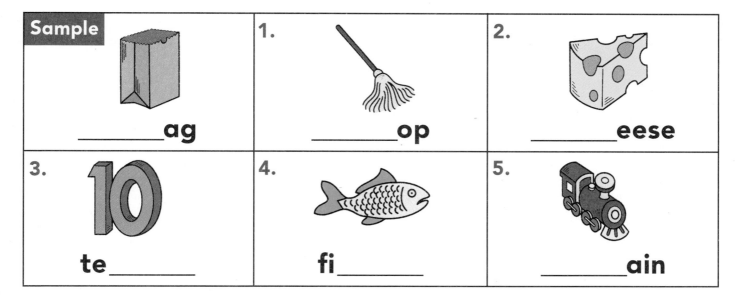

Sample	1.	2.
_____ag	_____op	_____eese
3.	**4.**	**5.**
te_____	fi_____	_____ain

B. Phonic Analysis: Vowels

Look at each picture.
Write the missing letter or letters on the blank line.

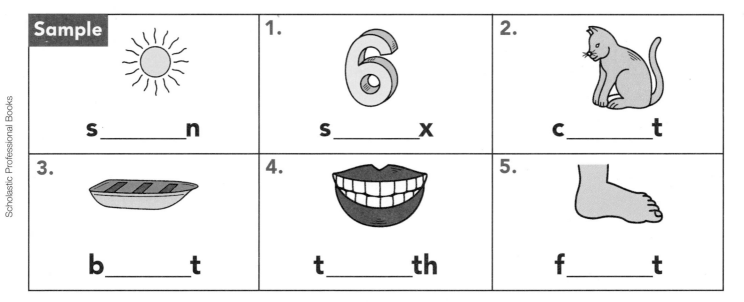

Sample	1.	2.
s_____n	s_____x	c_____t
3.	**4.**	**5.**
b_____t	t_____th	f_____t

C. High-Frequency Word Match
Circle the word your teacher says out loud.

Sample	1.	2.	3.
he	as	saw	when
me	is	see	where
we	it	said	way

D. Grammar, Usage, and Mechanics
Each sentence has two mistakes.
Write each sentence correctly on the blank line.

Sample the dog is furry

_____

_____

1. he didnt like it.

_____

_____

2. can you runs fast?

_____

_____

3. Where can i play

_____

_____

E. Reading Sentences

Fill in the bubble next to the sentence that tells about each picture.

Sample	
	○ A boy sits. ○ A boy sleeps. ○ A boy runs.
1.	○ She wears red socks. ○ She put the rock in the box. ○ She put the sock in the box.
2.	○ The nest has six eggs. ○ The net has a fish in it. ○ The nest has ten eggs.
3.	○ She likes to swim. ○ She plays on the swing. ○ She pets the small dog.
4.	○ It rained all day. ○ The train is fast. ○ The truck can go fast.

F. Story Comprehension
Read the story. Then answer each question.
Fill in the bubble next to the best answer.

> Tom likes to read. He reads books about cats. They can climb tall trees. He reads books about dogs. They like to wag their tails. He reads books about fish. They swim in the sea. Tom reads a lot of books.

1. What does Tom like to do?
- ◯ fish
- ◯ read
- ◯ play

2. What is a good title (name) for this story?
- ◯ Good Homes for Pets
- ◯ Cat and Mouse Books
- ◯ Books Tom Reads

3. What does Tom read about?
- ◯ school
- ◯ toys
- ◯ animals

4. Which book might Tom most like to read?
- ◯ Fun Games to Play
- ◯ Pet Rabbits
- ◯ Bikes and Skates

Scholastic Professional Books

Reading Skills Practice Test 7

A. Phonic Analysis: Consonants

Look at each picture.
Write the missing letter or letters on the blank line.

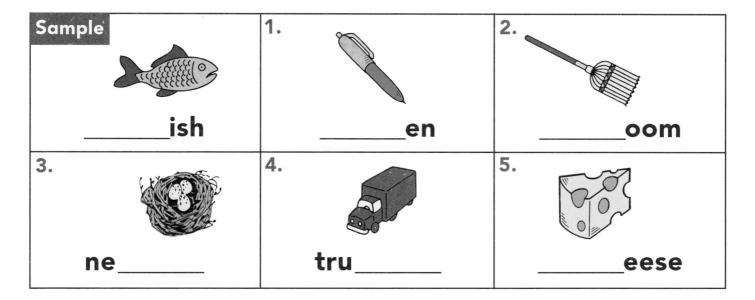

Sample	1.	2.
_____ish	_____en	_____oom
3.	**4.**	**5.**
ne_____	tru_____	_____eese

B. Phonic Analysis: Vowels

Look at each picture.
Write the missing letter or letters on the blank line.

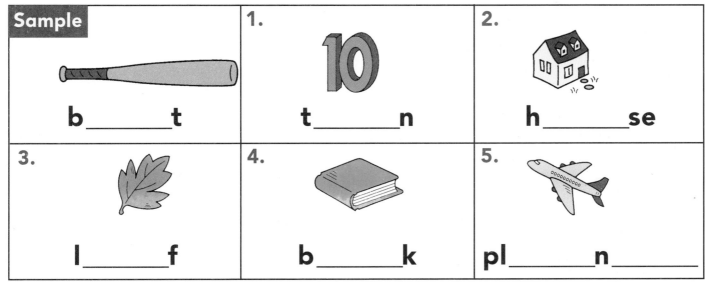

Sample	1.	2.
b_____t	t_____n	h_____se
3.	**4.**	**5.**
l_____f	b_____k	pl_____n_____

C. High-Frequency Word Match
Circle the word your teacher says out loud.

Sample	1.	2.	3.
in	hat	some	wet
and	his	come	where
are	has	could	what

D. Grammar, Usage, and Mechanics
Each sentence has two mistakes.
Write each sentence correctly on the blank line.

Sample the cat sleeps

_____

- -

_____

1. why cant we go?

_____

- -

_____

2. They plays all day

_____

- -

_____

3. Can sam sit with us

_____

- -

_____

E. Reading Sentences

Fill in the bubble next to the sentence
that tells about each picture.

Sample		○ The boy hits the ball. ○ The boy kicks the ball. ○ The boy throws the ball.
1.		○ The duck sits on a rock. ○ The dog runs by the lake. ○ The duck swims in the pond.
2.		○ She rides her bike. ○ The girl has a big kite. ○ They have a new bike.
3.		○ The branch has five leaves. ○ The tree has no leaves. ○ The leaf fell off the branch.
4.		○ He sits next to the cow. ○ He can see the cow. ○ He is near a horse.

Scholastic Professional Books

F. Story Comprehension
Read the story. Then answer each question.
Fill in the bubble next to the best answer.

> The wind helps people. The wind helps people to fly kites. The wind also helps people to sail boats. The wind helps plants, too. The wind blows plant seeds to new places. Soon, the seeds grow. Then there are new plants.

1. What is a good title (name) for this story?
- ○ How to Sail a Boat
- ○ The Wind
- ○ Growing Plants

2. How does the wind help people?
- ○ to fly a kite
- ○ to make a book
- ○ to make a boat

3. What happens after the wind blows plant seeds?
- ○ rocks grow
- ○ seeds grow
- ○ people grow

4. What other thing do you think the wind can do?
- ○ make a kite
- ○ blow away a leaf
- ○ be a home for animals

Scholastic Professional Books

Reading Skills Practice Test 8

A. Phonic Analysis: Consonants
Look at each picture.
Write the missing letter or letters on the line.

Sample	1.	2.
_____esk	_____an	_____ee
3.	4.	5.
_____ip	clo_____	ha_____

B. Phonic Analysis: Vowels
Look at each picture.
Write the missing letter or letters on the line.

Sample	1.	2.
n_____t	c_____p	m_____n
3.	4.	5.
cl_____d	b_____t	r_____k_____

C. Vocabulary: Picture-Word Match

Fill in the bubble next to the word that names each picture.

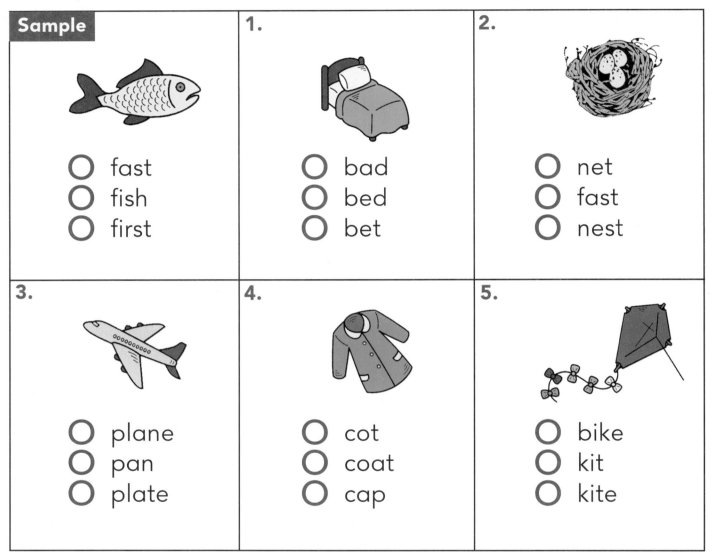

Sample	**1.**	**2.**
○ fast ○ fish ○ first	○ bad ○ bed ○ bet	○ net ○ fast ○ nest
3.	**4.**	**5.**
○ plane ○ pan ○ plate	○ cot ○ coat ○ cap	○ bike ○ kit ○ kite

D. High-Frequency Word Match

Circle the word your teacher says out loud.

Sample	**1.**	**2.**	**3.**	**4.**	**5.**
it in out	him he his	when they then	said says say	are our your	who was what

Scholastic Professional Books

E. Grammar, Usage, and Mechanics

Each sentence has two mistakes.
Write each sentence correctly on the blank line.

Sample he ride in a plane.

----

1. she runs very fast

----

2. where are my socks

----

3. We plays with the dog

F. Story Comprehension

Read the story. Then answer each question.
Fill in the bubble next to the best answer.

> Have you ever seen a rabbit? Rabbits come in many colors. Their fur can be brown, black, white, or gray. Rabbits have long ears to help them hear sounds from far away.
>
> Rabbits can be wild animals or pets. Wild rabbits live in holes in the ground. Pet rabbits live in homes with people.

1. What is a good title (name) for this story?
- ○ Colors
- ○ Rabbits
- ○ Wild Animals

2. What do a rabbit's long ears help it to do?
- ○ hear sounds from far away
- ○ make holes in the ground
- ○ see things that are far away

3. Where are two places rabbits can live?
- ○ on land and in the sea
- ○ in holes in the ground and in people's homes
- ○ in people's homes and in treetops

4. Write a sentence telling something about rabbits.

_____

- -

_____

_____

- -

_____

Scholastic Professional Books

Reading Skills Practice Test 9

A. Phonic Analysis: Consonants
Look at each picture.
Write the missing letters on the line.

Sample _____ess	**1.** _____ain	**2.** _____ag
3. la_____	**4.** de_____	**5.** _____oon

B. Phonic Analysis: Vowels
Look at each picture.
Write the missing letter or letters on the line.

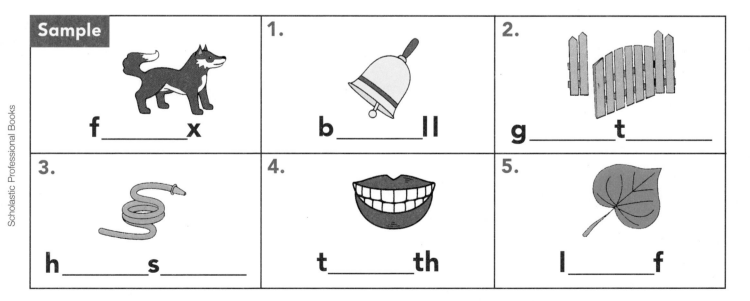

Sample f_____x	**1.** b_____ll	**2.** g_____t
3. h_____s_____	**4.** t_____th	**5.** l_____f

C. High-Frequency Word Match

Fill in the bubble next to the word your teacher says out loud.

Sample	1.	2.	3.	4.	5.
○ him ○ her ○ house	○ very ○ vine ○ cherry	○ small ○ song ○ some	○ true ○ that ○ there	○ which ○ what ○ where	○ between ○ because ○ bacon

D. Vocabulary: Picture-Word Match

Fill in the bubble next to the word that names each picture.

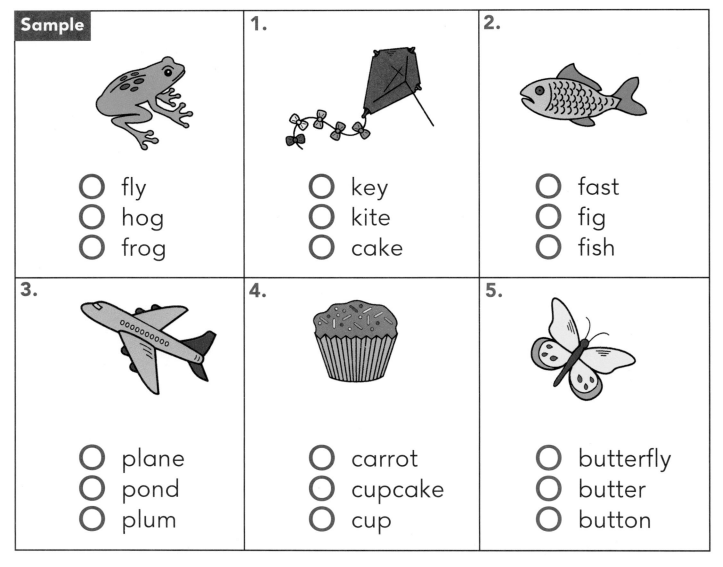

Sample
○ fly
○ hog
○ frog

1.
○ key
○ kite
○ cake

2.
○ fast
○ fig
○ fish

3.
○ plane
○ pond
○ plum

4.
○ carrot
○ cupcake
○ cup

5.
○ butterfly
○ butter
○ button

E. Grammar, Usage, and Mechanics

Read each sentence. Fill in the bubble next to the word or words that best complete each sentence.

Sample

_____ walk to school.
- ○ we
- ○ look
- ○ We

1. My kitten likes to _____
- ○ jump.
- ○ jump?
- ○ Jump

2. I went to see _____ for a checkup.
- ○ dr. Jones
- ○ Dr. Jones
- ○ dr. jones

3. May _____ play with you?
- ○ i
- ○ It
- ○ I

4. My family went to _____ on a trip.
- ○ New York
- ○ NEW YORK
- ○ new york

5. The girl _____ the bus.
- ○ ride
- ○ rides
- ○ rided

Scholastic Professional Books

F. Story Comprehension
Read the story. Then answer each question.
Fill in the bubble next to the best answer.

Jane Goodall

Jane Goodall is a famous scientist. She learned about wild chimpanzees in Africa.

Jane learned that baby chimpanzees ride on their mothers' backs until they are 3 years old. She learned that chimpanzees hold hands like people do. She also learned that chimpanzees use sticks to catch insects. Jane learned all about chimpanzees by watching them closely.

1. What is a good title for this story?
   ○ Scientists
   ○ Jane Goodall
   ○ Baby Chimpanzees

2. Where did Jane Goodall learn about chimpanzees?
   ○ Africa
   ○ South America
   ○ Asia

3. Baby chimpanzees ride on their mothers' backs until what age?
   ○ 5 years old
   ○ 6 months old
   ○ 3 years old

4. Write a sentence telling something that Jane Goodall learned about chimpanzees.

_____

_____

_____

Scholastic Professional Books

MICHAEL NEUGEBAUER/COURTESY OF NORTH-SOUTH BOOKS

Reading Skills Practice Test 10

A. Phonic Analysis: Consonants

Look at each picture.
Write the missing letter or letters on the blank line.

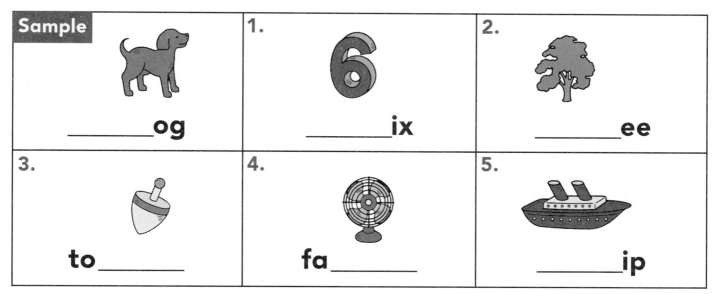

Sample	1.	2.
_____og	_____ix	_____ee
3.	4.	5.
to_____	fa_____	_____ip

B. Phonic Analysis: Vowels

Look at each picture.
Write the missing letter or letters on the blank line.

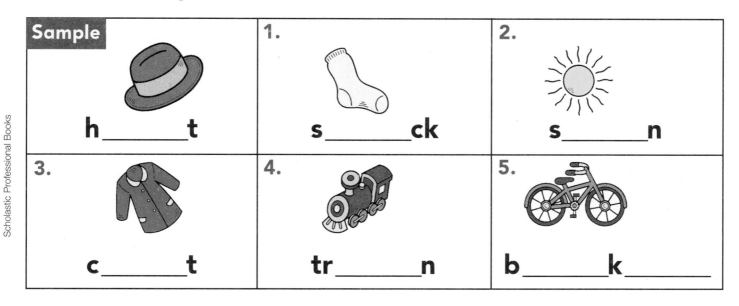

Sample	1.	2.
h_____t	s_____ck	s_____n
3.	4.	5.
c_____t	tr_____n	b_____k

C. High-Frequency Word Match
Circle the word your teacher says out loud.

Sample	1.	2.	3.
the	as	had	see
me	is	has	sad
to	it	have	said

D. Grammar, Usage, and Mechanics
Each sentence has two mistakes.
Write each sentence correctly on the blank line.

Sample the boy is happy

_____

- -

_____

1. she cant help us.

_____

- -

_____

2. can we plays ball?

_____

- -

_____

3. Where will i go

_____

- -

_____

Scholastic Professional Books

Reading Skills Practice Test 11

A. Phonic Analysis: Consonants

Look at each picture.
Write the missing letters on the line.

Sample	1.	2.
_____oor	_____ant	_____elve
3.	**4.**	**5.**
_____umb	_____eakers	ben_____

B. Phonic Analysis: Vowels

Look at each picture.
Write the missing letter or letters on the line.

Sample	1.	2.
g_____rl	m_____se	g_____m_____
3.	**4.**	**5.**
b_____tton	sk_____t_____s	_____gg

C. High-Frequency Word Match

Fill in the bubble next to the word your teacher says out loud.

Sample	1.	2.	3.	4.	5.
○ sad	○ fat	○ like	○ sit	○ up	○ black
○ said	○ fit	○ lick	○ sat	○ on	○ book
○ send	○ that	○ luck	○ set	○ of	○ blue

D. Vocabulary: Picture-Word Match

Fill in the bubble next to the word that names each picture.

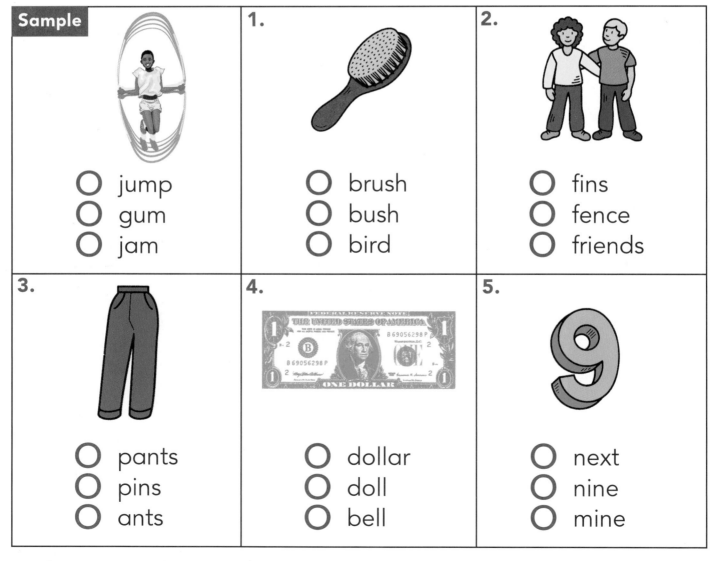

Sample
○ jump
○ gum
○ jam

1.
○ brush
○ bush
○ bird

2.
○ fins
○ fence
○ friends

3.
○ pants
○ pins
○ ants

4.
○ dollar
○ doll
○ bell

5.
○ next
○ nine
○ mine

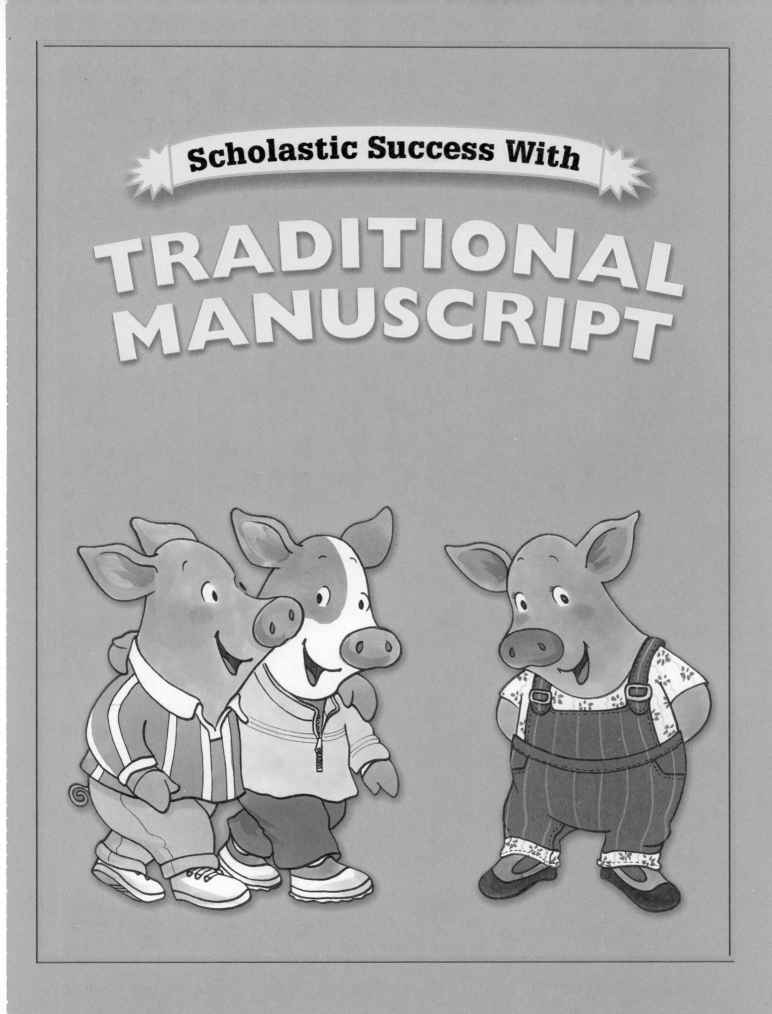

Scholastic Success With

TRADITIONAL MANUSCRIPT

Name _Madeline_

A a

Trace and write.

A A A A

a a a a

Aa Aa Aa

Adam Ape is active.

Adam Ape is active

Annie asked Alice.

Amie asked Alice

B b

Trace and write.

B B B

b b b b

Bb B b b Bb

Betsy bee buzzes.

Betsy bee buzzes.

Bobby buys balloons.

Bobby buys balloons

Cc

Trace and write.

C C C C

c c c c c

Cc

Cows crave color.

Callie carries cats.

Dd

Trace and write.

D D D D

d d d d

Dd

Dandy Duck dances.

Dragons draw dogs.

Ee

Trace and write.

E E E E E

e e e e e

Ee

Ellie Emu is elegant.

Ed eats eight eggs.

F f

Trace and write.

F F F

f f f

Ff

Fran Fish is funny.

Footballs fly fast.

G g

Trace and write.

G G G

g g g g

Gg

Hee
Hee
Hee

Gus Goose giggles.

Greta grows greens.

Scholastic Professional Books

Hh

Trace and write.

H H H H

h h h h

Hh

Hal Hippo is happy.

Hannah hangs hats.

I i

Trace and write.

I I I I

i i i i

I i

Irina Iguana is itchy.

Invite Irving inside.

Jj

Trace and write.

J   J J   J J

j   j j j j

Jj

Jim Jellyfish is jazzy.

Jill juggles jelly jars.

K k

Trace and write.

K K K K

k k k k

K k

Kyle Kangaroo kicks.

Katie keeps kittens.

Scholastic Professional Books

LI

Trace and write.

L L L L

I I I I

LI

Lyle Lion looks lost.

Lindy loves lollipops.

M m

Trace and write.

M M M

m m m

Mm

Mike Mouse is messy.

Mom met Madeline.

Scholastic Professional Books

N n

Trace and write.

N N N N

n n n n

Nn

Nikki Newt needs naps.

_____

Nurse Ned nibbles.

_____

O o

Trace and write.

O O O

O O O O

O o

Opal Owl sings opera.

Otis orders oranges.

Pp

Trace and write.

P P P

p p p p

Pp

Pam Pig paid a penny.

Peter Pig says please.

Q q

Trace and write.

Q Q Q

q q q

Q q

Quinn Quail is quiet.

Quebec is quite nice.

shhhh!

R r

Trace and write.

R R R R

r r r r

R r

Randy Rabbit races.

Robin reads rapidly.

S s

Trace and write.

S S S S

s s s s

S s

Susanna Seal stars.

Sam sees sailboats.

Scholastic Professional Books

Tt

Trace and write.

Tristan Toad is toothy.

Tigers taste terrible.

Uu

Trace and write.

U U U U

u u u u

Uu

Ula uses an umbrella.

Uncle Uno umpires.

Scholastic Professional Books

V v

Trace and write.

V V V

V V V V

V v

Vic Vulture is vain.

Vegetables vary.

W w

Trace and write.

W W W W

w w w w

Ww

Will Worm is wealthy.

Wilma wipes windows.

X x

Trace and write.

X̶a̶v̶i̶e̶r̶ ̶F̶o̶x̶ ̶i̶s̶ ̶e̶x̶c̶i̶t̶e̶d̶.̶

X̶e̶n̶i̶a̶ ̶O̶x̶ ̶e̶x̶i̶t̶s̶.̶

Yy

Trace and write.

Y Y Y

y y y y

Yy

Yvonne Yak yawns.

Young yaks yodel.

Z z

Trace and write.

Z Z Z Z Z

z z z z z

Z z

Zoe Zebra is zany.

Zed zooms at the zoo.

A–Z

Trace and write.

A B C D E F G H I

J K L M N O P Q

R S T U V W X Y Z

ABCD

a–z

Trace and write.

a   b   c   d   e

f   g   h   i   j   k
            J

l   m   n   o   p

q   r   s   t   u

v   w   x   y   z

abcd

1-5

Trace and write.

6–10

Trace and write.

Color Words

Trace and write.

red   red red red

yellow yellow

blue   blue

green green

orange orange

yellow

red

blue

green

orange

More Color Words

Trace and write.

purple   purple

brown   brown

black   black

white   white

pink   pink

pink

white

brown

purple

black

Number Words

Trace and write.

one   two   three   four   five

1 one

2 two

3 three

4 four

5 five

More Number Words

Trace and write.

six

eight

ten

seven

nine

6 six

7 seven

8 eight

9 nine

10 ten

Scholastic Professional Books

Shapes

Trace and write.

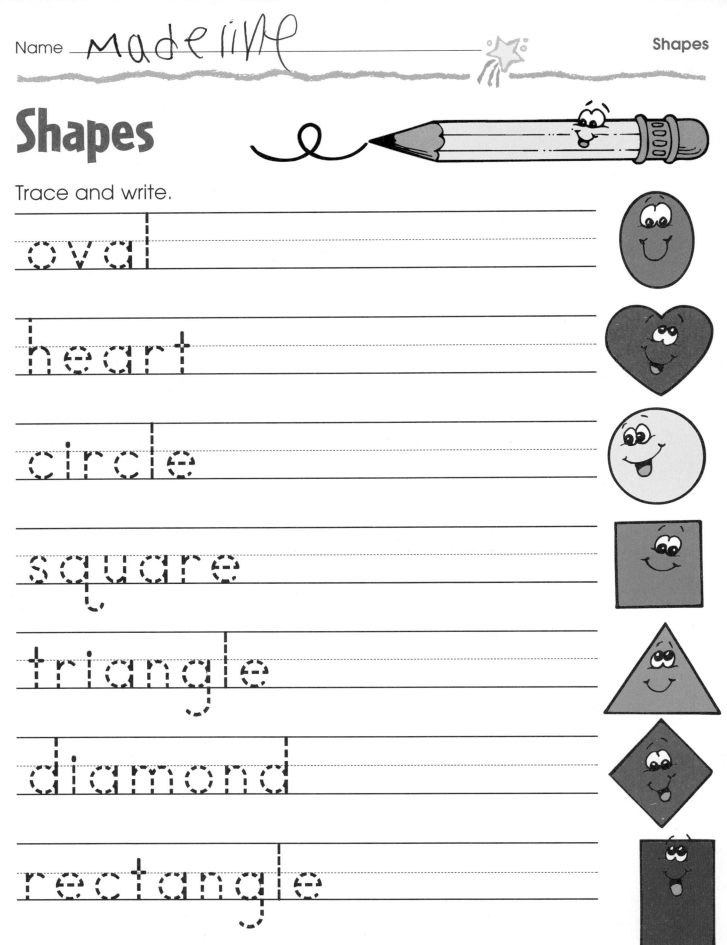

oval

heart

circle

square

triangle

diamond

rectangle

Scholastic Professional Books

Days of the Week

Trace and write.

Sunday   Sunday

Monday   Monday

Tuesday   Tuesday

Wednesday   Wednesday

Thursday   Thurs

Friday

Saturday

Months

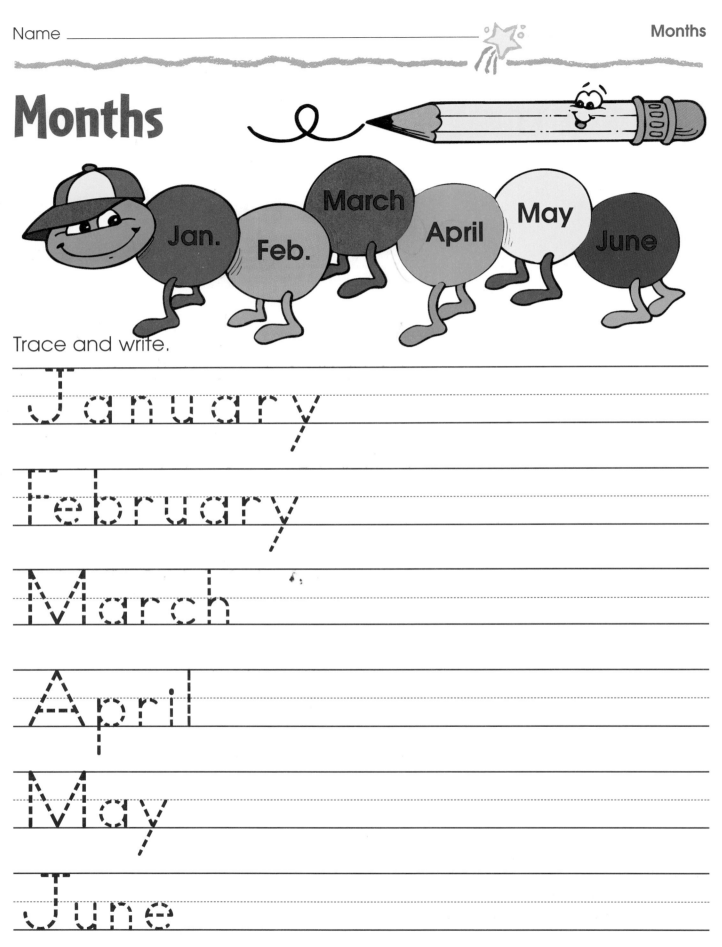

Trace and write.

January

February

March

April

May

June

Months

Trace and write.

July

August

September

October

November

December

Special Days

Write each special day.

JAN. FEB. MAR. APRIL MAY JUN. JULY

New Year's Day

_____

Valentine's Day

_____

Presidents' Day

_____

St. Patrick's Day

_____

Mother's Day

_____

Father's Day

_____

Fourth of July

_____

Scholastic Professional Books

Special Days

Write each special day.

AUG   SEPT   OCT   NOV   DEC

Labor Day

Halloween

Veterans Day

Thanksgiving

Hannukah

Christmas

Kwanzaa

Animals From A to Z

Write the animal names on the lines below.

alligator
bear
cougar
duck

elk
frog
giraffe
horse

iguana
jaguar
kangaroo
leopard

moose
newt
ostrich

Animals From A to Z

Write the animal names on the lines below.

parrot
quail
raccoon

squirrel
tiger
urchin

vulture
whale
X-ray fish

yak
zebra

The Continents

Write the names of the continents.

Africa
_____
_____

Asia
_____
_____

Australia
_____
_____

Antarctica
_____
_____

Europe
_____
_____

North America
_____
_____

South America
_____
_____

Africa

Asia

Antarctica

Australia

Europe

North America

South America

The Planets

Write the names of these planets.

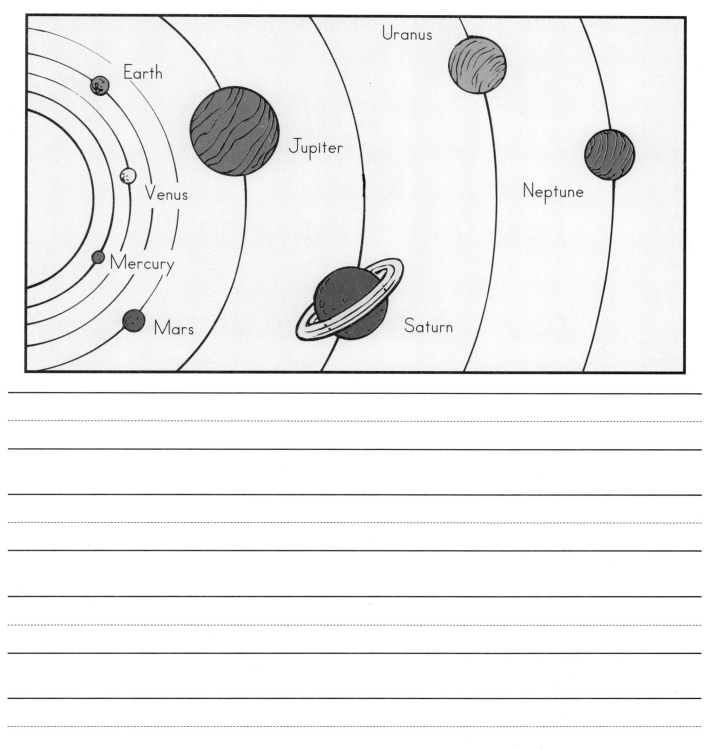

_____
- -
_____

_____
- -
_____

_____
- -
_____

_____
- -
_____

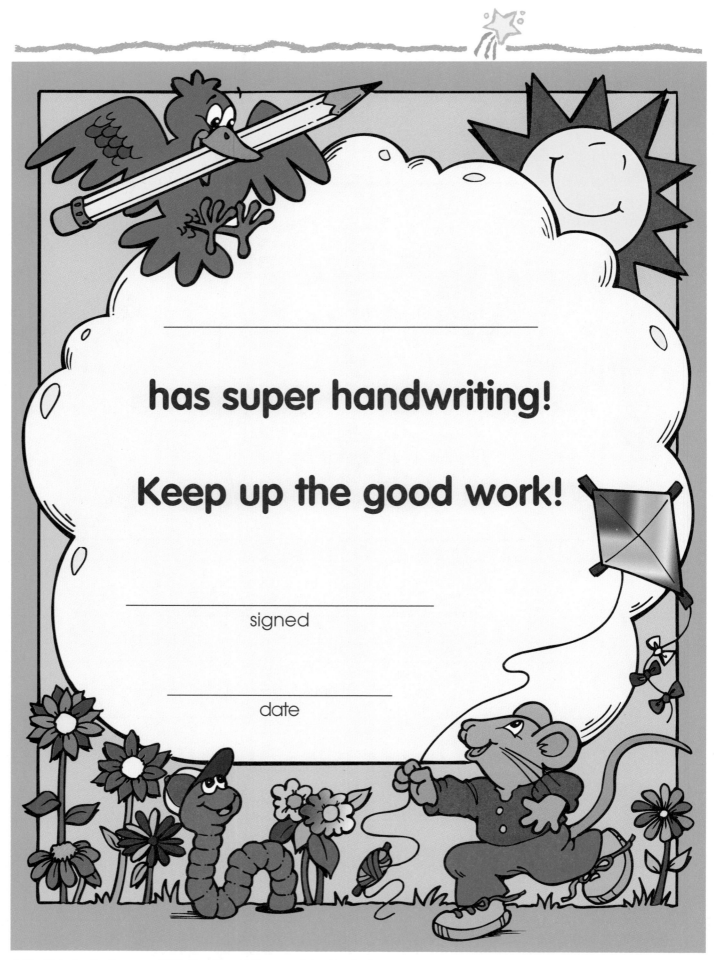

has super handwriting!

Keep up the good work!

_____

signed

_____

date

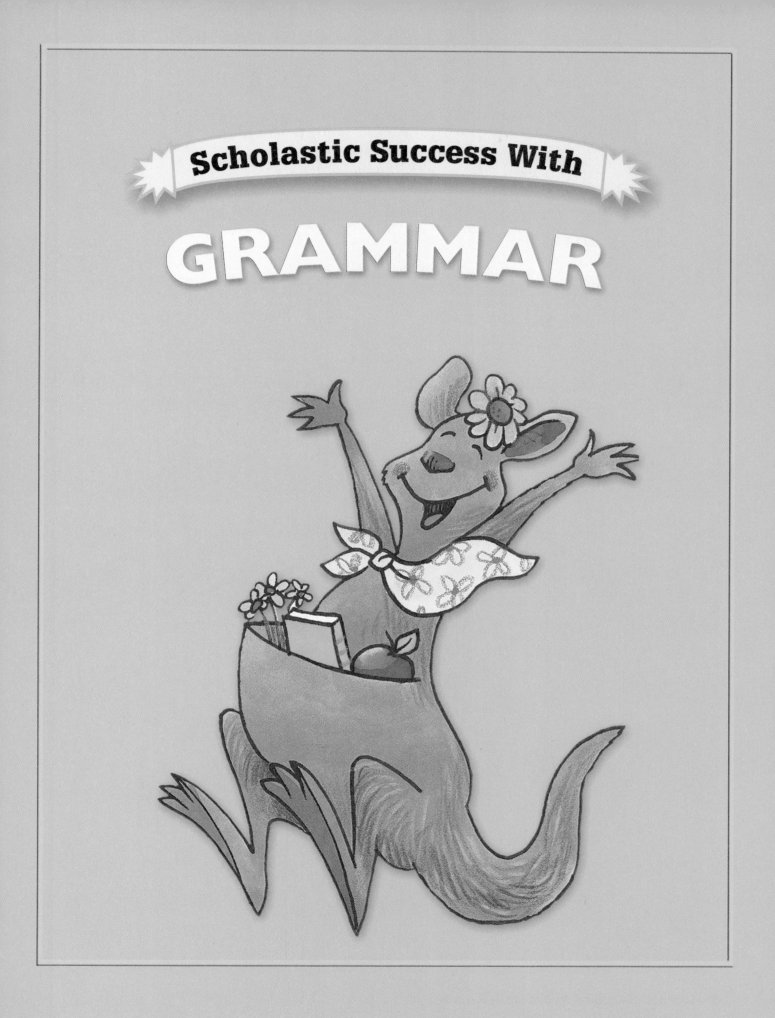

Scholastic Success With

GRAMMAR

Capitalizing First Word

A sentence always begins with a capital letter.

Draw a line under the first letter in each sentence.
Read each sentence to a friend.

1 **The cat sat on a rat.**   **2** **The rat sat on a hat.**

3 **The hat is on the dog.**   **4** **The dog is on a mat.**

Scholastic Professional Books

Capitalizing First Word

A sentence always begins with a capital letter.

Copy each sentence correctly on the line.

1 the cat sat.

_____

- - - - - - - - - - - - - - - - - - -

_____

2 the dog sat.

_____

- - - - - - - - - - - - - - - - - - -

_____

3 i see the cat.

_____

- - - - - - - - - - - - - - - - - - -

_____

4 i can see.

_____

- - - - - - - - - - - - - - - - - - -

_____

Capitalizing First Word

Read each sentence. Then fill in the circle next to the word with the capital letter that begins the sentence.

1 **The cat is in the van.**
- ⬭ cat
- ⬭ The

2 **My dog can run.**
- ⬭ My
- ⬭ dog

3 **Jan can hop.**
- ⬭ Jan
- ⬭ hop

4 **I like ham.**
- ⬭ ham
- ⬭ I

5 **Ants like jam.**
- ⬭ jam
- ⬭ Ants

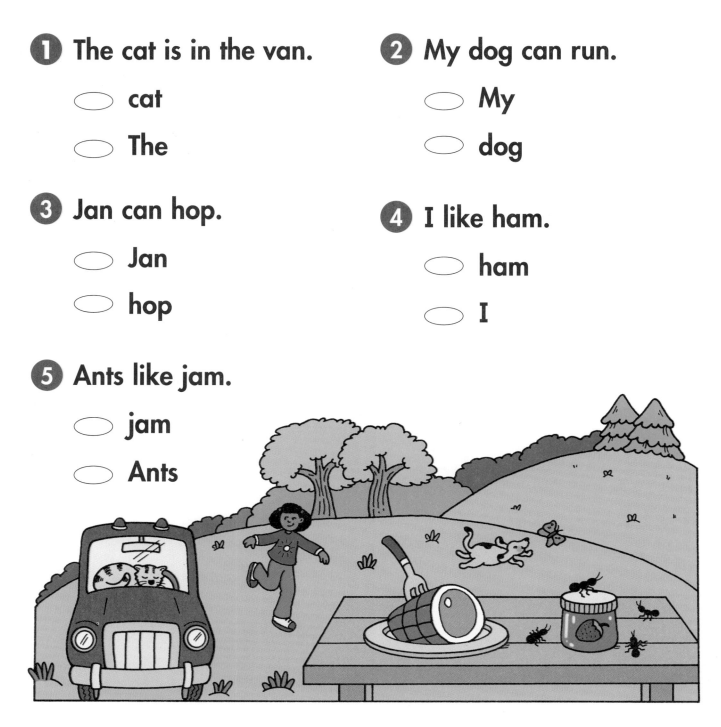

Scholastic Professional Books

Periods

A telling sentence ends with a period.

Circle the period at the end of each sentence.

1 I see Jan.

2 I go with Jan.

3 We see Dan.

4 I go with Dan and Jan.

Draw a line under the last word in each sentence.
Add a period to each sentence.

5 We go to school

6 We like school

Periods

 A telling sentence ends with a period.

Write a period where it belongs in each sentence. Read the sentences to a friend.

1 **Dan is in the cab**

2 **The cat is in the cab**

3 **Mom is in the cab**

4 **We see Dan and Mom**

Read the words. Write each word at the end of the correct sentence.

van.   red.

5 **We can go in the** _____

6 **The van is** _____

Periods

Read each group of words. Fill in the circle next to the correct sentence.

1
- ◯ The cat is on the mat.
- ◯ the cat is on the mat
- ◯ the cat on the mat

2
- ◯ the rat is on the mop
- ◯ the rat is on the mop
- ◯ The rat is on the mop.

3
- ◯ The rat sees the cat
- ◯ The rat sees the cat.
- ◯ the rat sees the cat

4
- ◯ The rat can hop.
- ◯ The rat can hop
- ◯ the rat can hop

5
- ◯ the cat and rat sit
- ◯ The cat and rat sit
- ◯ The cat and rat sit.

Capitalizing I

Always write the word I with a capital letter.

Circle the word **I** in each sentence.

1 I like to hop.

2 Pam and I like to hop.

3 I can hop to Mom.

4 Mom and I can hop.

Draw what you like. Use the word **I** to write about it.

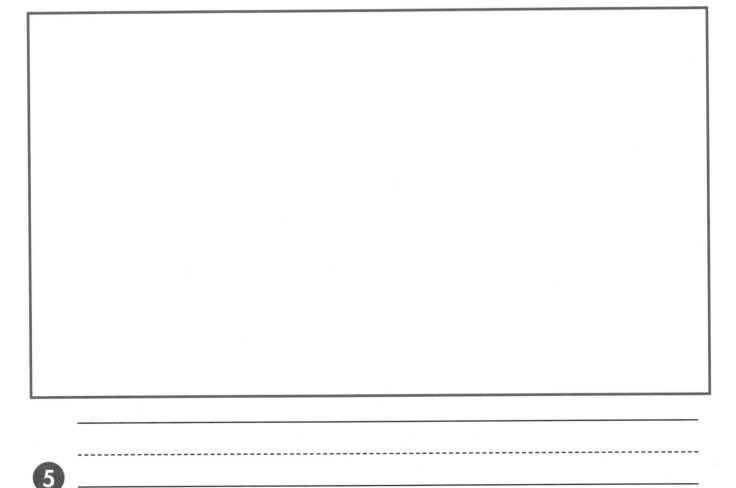

5 _____

Capitalizing <u>I</u>

Always write the word <u>I</u> with a capital letter.

Read the sentences. Write <u>I</u> on the line.

1 _____ will ride.

2 _____ will swim.

3 Mom and _____ will sing.

4 Then _____ will read.

What will you do next? Write it on the line.

5 I will _____

Capitalizing I

Read each group of words. Fill in the circle next to the correct sentence.

1
- ◯ i sit on a mat.
- ◯ I sit on a mat.
- ◯ i sit on a mat

2
- ◯ Pam and I like cats.
- ◯ Pam and i like cats.
- ◯ pam and i like cats

3
- ◯ I see the van.
- ◯ i see the van.
- ◯ i see the van

4
- ◯ i like jam.
- ◯ i like jam
- ◯ I like jam.

5
- ◯ i like to nap.
- ◯ I like to nap.
- ◯ i like to nap

Simple Sentences

 A sentence tells a complete idea.

Circle who or what each sentence is about.

1 Pam ran.

2 Dan hops.

3 The cat sits.

4 The van can go.

Draw a line from each sentence to the picture
of who or what the sentence is about.

5 Jan is hot.

6 The hat is on top.

7 The man sat.

Simple Sentences

A sentence tells a complete idea.

Circle each sentence.

1 **Bill**
Bill paints.

2 **likes to read**
Tom likes to read.

3 **plants flowers**
Pat plants flowers.

Finish the sentence.

4 I like _____

Simple Sentences

Read each group of words. Fill in the circle next to the complete sentence.

1

◯ on a mat

◯ The cat sits on a mat.

◯ The cat

2

◯ Pam and Dan like jam.

◯ Pam and Dan

◯ like jam

3

◯ I see Mom.

◯ I see

◯ Mom

4

◯ my hat

◯ I like

◯ I like my hat.

5

◯ Ben.

◯ Ben can hop.

◯ hop

Word Order

 Words in a sentence must be in an order that makes sense.

Read each group of words. Draw a line under the word that should go first in each sentence.

1 dots. I like

2 Pam dots. likes

3 like We hats.

4 hats with dots. We like

Now write each group of words in the right order.

1 _____

2 _____

3 _____

4 _____

Word Order

Words in a sentence must be in an order that makes sense.

Read each group of words. Write them in the right order on the lines.

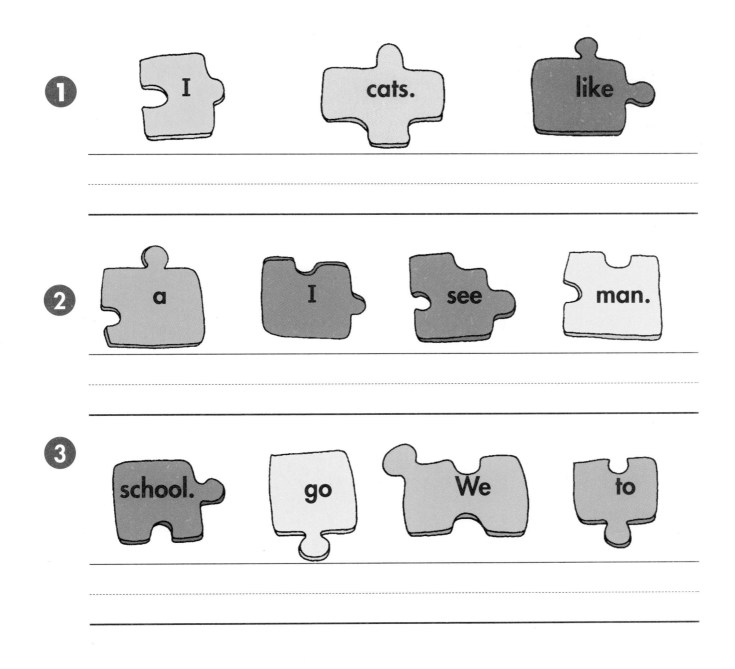

1   I   cats.   like

2   a   I   see   man.

3   school.   go   We   to

To the Teacher: Remind children that a sentence begins with a capital letter.
Point out that a telling sentence ends with a period.

Word Order

Read each group of words. Fill in the circle next to the words that are in an order that makes sense.

1
- ◯ I red dots. see
- ◯ I see red dots.
- ◯ dots red

2
- ◯ Dan is in a big van.
- ◯ big Dan a van. is in
- ◯ van big Dan in a is

3
- ◯ fat. cat The is
- ◯ is fat. The cat
- ◯ The cat is fat.

4
- ◯ We like the hat.
- ◯ the like hat. We
- ◯ We hat. the like

5
- ◯ likes Ben jam.
- ◯ Ben likes jam.
- ◯ jam. likes Ben

Question Sentences

Question sentences ask something.

Read each sentence. Circle each question mark.

1 Who hid the hat?

2 Is it on the cat?

3 Can you see the hat?

4 Is it on the man?

Write two questions. Draw a line under each capital letter at the beginning of each question. Circle the question marks.

5 _____

_____

6 _____

_____

Scholastic Professional Books

Question Sentences

Question sentences ask something.

Draw a line under each sentence that asks a question.
Circle the question mark.

1 Who hid the cat?

2 Can the cat see the rat?

3 The cat is in the van.

4 Can the van go?

Read the sentences. Circle each sentence that asks something.

5 Can we sit in the van?

We can sit in the van.

6 Dan can nap in the van.

Can Dan nap in the van?

Scholastic Professional Books

Question Sentences

Read the sentences. Fill in the circle next to the sentence that asks a question.

1

◯ Who hid my hat?

◯ My hat is with him.

◯ My hat is big.

2

◯ The hat has spots.

◯ The hat has dots.

◯ Did the hat have dots?

3

◯ Jan likes my hat.

◯ Did Jan like my hat?

◯ Jan did like my hat.

4

◯ Can you see the hat?

◯ You can see the hat.

◯ She can see the hat.

5

◯ Dan can get a hat.

◯ Dan likes hats.

◯ Dan has the hat?

Naming Words

 A naming word names a person, place, or thing.

Read each sentence. Draw a line under the word or words that name the person, place, or thing in each sentence.

1 The pig is big.

2 The pan is hot.

3 Pam hid.

4 Can you run up the hill?

Draw a line from each sentence to the picture that shows the naming word in that sentence.

5 The sun is hot.

6 Sam ran and ran.

7 Is the cat fat?

Naming Words

 A naming word names a person, place, or thing.

Circle the naming words in the sentences.

1 **Al can go in a van.**

2 **The cat sat on a mat.**

3 **Pat ran up the hill.**

4 **Dan and Jan will mop.**

Draw a picture of a person, place, or thing. Write a sentence about your picture. Circle the naming word.

Naming Words

Read each sentence. Fill in the circle next to the naming word.

1 I see a big cat.

ⓐ see   ⓑ big   ⓒ cat

2 The rat ran fast.

ⓐ ran   ⓑ rat   ⓒ fast

3 Can you see the map?

ⓐ Can   ⓑ map   ⓒ see

4 The van is tan.

ⓐ van   ⓑ is   ⓒ tan

5 The fan is not on!

ⓐ not   ⓑ on   ⓒ fan

Capitalizing Special Names

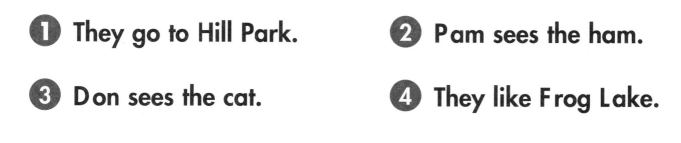

The names of people, places, and pets are special. They begin with capital letters.

Draw a line under the special name in each sentence. Then circle the first letter or letters in that name.

1 They go to Hill Park.

2 Pam sees the ham.

3 Don sees the cat.

4 They like Frog Lake.

Write a special name of a person, place, or pet you know.

5 _____

Capitalizing Special Names

 The names of people, places, and pets are special. They begin with capital letters.

Circle each special name. Draw a line under each capital letter in each name.

1 I am Pam.

2 I sit on Ant Hill.

3 Ron likes the lake.

4 He likes Bat Lake.

Read the special names in the box.
Write a special name for each picture.

| Spot   Hill Street |

5 _____

_____

6 _____

_____

Capitalizing Special Names

Read each sentence. Fill in the circle next to the special name.

1 Can Don go to the picnic?

- ◯ picnic
- ◯ Don
- ◯ Can

2 The picnic will be on Pig Hill.

- ◯ Pig Hill
- ◯ picnic
- ◯ The

3 The hill is on Jam Street.

- ◯ hill
- ◯ The
- ◯ Jam Street

4 Jan will go to the picnic.

- ◯ go
- ◯ picnic
- ◯ Jan

5 She will go in Ham Lake.

- ◯ She
- ◯ Ham Lake
- ◯ will

Action Words

 An action word tells what happens.

Read each sentence. Circle the word that tells what happens.

1 The hen sits.

2 The cat ran.

3 Pam hid.

4 The dog naps.

Read the words. Use the words to finish the sentences.

run	see

5 I will _____ up the hill.

6 I _____ a big pig.

Action Words

 An action word tells what happens.

Look at each picture. Read the words. Write the action word.

1 I can see.

2 The cat sits.

3 Mom mops.

4 We run fast.

5 It hops a lot.

Action Words

Read each sentence.
Fill in the circle next to the action word.

1 **I sit on a hill.**

    ⓐ I   ⓑ sit   ⓒ hill

2 **The rat ran fast.**

    ⓐ ran   ⓑ rat   ⓒ fast

3 **We mop a lot.**

    ⓐ We   ⓑ lot   ⓒ mop

4 **The dog digs up sand.**

    ⓐ dog   ⓑ sand   ⓒ digs

5 **Pam hops up and down.**

    ⓐ hops   ⓑ up   ⓒ Pam

Describing Words

A describing word tells more about a person, place, or thing.

Read each sentence. Circle the
word that tells about the cat.

1 I see a **big** cat.

2 The **fast** cat ran.

3 My cat is **bad**.

4 The **fat** cat naps.

Look at each cat. Circle the word that tells about it.

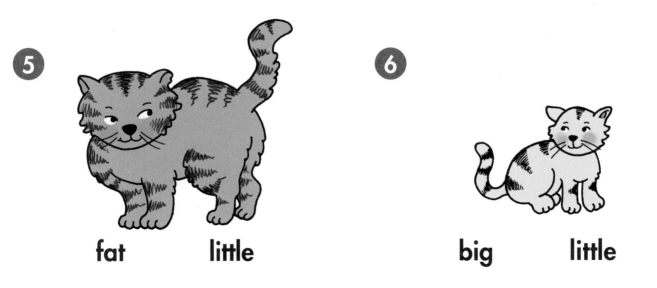

5 fat   little

6 big   little

Describing Words

A describing word tells more about a person, place, or thing.

Look at each picture. Circle the words that tell about it.

1

big   fast

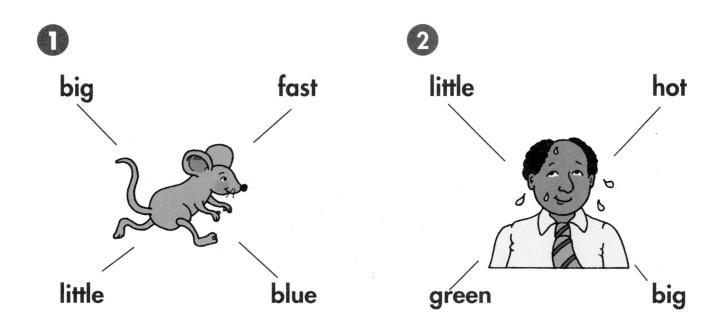

little   blue

2

little   hot

green   big

Draw a line between each sentence and the picture that shows what it describes.

3 It is fat.

4 They are little.

Describing Words

Read each sentence. Fill in the circle next to the describing word.

1 The silly cat can play.

- ◯ silly
- ◯ cat
- ◯ play

2 The bad rat will run.

- ◯ bad
- ◯ run
- ◯ rat

3 The black dog naps.

- ◯ dog
- ◯ black
- ◯ naps

4 The cow is big.

- ◯ cow
- ◯ is
- ◯ big

5 A green frog can hop.

- ◯ frog
- ◯ green
- ◯ hop

Telling Sentences

A telling sentence tells something.

Circle the capital letter at the beginning of each telling sentence.
Then circle the period at the end of each telling sentence.

1 I see the basket.

2 The cat is in the basket.

3 Hats can go in it.

4 The sock can go in it.

Draw a line under each telling sentence.

5 I can fill the basket.

6 Can you get the mop?

7 We can clean.

Telling Sentences

 A telling sentence tells something.

Draw a line to match each sentence with the picture that shows what the sentence tells.

1 She has a mop.

2 The dog is on top.

3 Dan gets the hats.

4 Ron can clean spots.

Read the sentences. Circle the capital letter and period in the telling sentence.

5 Put it in the pot.   **6** Is it in the pan?

Scholastic Professional Books

Telling Sentences

Read the sentences. Fill in the circle next to each sentence that tells something.

1

◯ Can you get the basket?

◯ You can get it.

◯ Can you fill it?

2

◯ The basket is big.

◯ Is the basket big?

◯ Why is it big?

3

◯ What can go in it?

◯ Will the hat go in?

◯ The hat is in the basket.

4

◯ A cat can not go in it.

◯ Can a cat go in?

◯ Will a cat go in it?

5

◯ Can we fill it?

◯ We can fill the basket.

◯ Will you fill it?

Exclamation Sentences

Exclamatory sentences show strong feelings such as excitement, surprise, or fear. They end with exclamation marks. (!)

Read each sentence. Circle each exclamation mark. Draw a line under the capital letter at the beginning of each sentence.

1 **Help! The rat is on top!**

2 **Get the cat!**

3 **This cat is bad!**

4 **Uh-oh! The cat is wet!**

Read each set of sentences. Draw a line under the sentence or sentences that show strong feeling.

5 **Oh my! Get the dog!**

Let's get the dog.

6 **The dog runs.**

Oh! The dog runs!

Exclamation Sentences

Choose the sentence in each pair that shows strong feeling. Write it on the line. Put an exclamation mark at the end.

> Exclamatory sentences show strong feeling, such as excitement, surprise, or fear. They end with an exclamation mark. (!)

1 Run to the show   We will go to the show

_____

2 I'm late for it   Oh my, I'm very late

_____

3 What a great show   I liked the show

_____

4 The floor is wet   Watch out, the floor is wet

_____

5 We had fun   Wow, we had lots of fun

_____

Scholastic Professional Books

Exclamation Sentences

Read each group of sentences. Fill in the circle next to the sentence or sentences that show strong feeling.

1
- ○ The cow is on the hill.
- ○ The cow likes grass.
- ○ Yes! The cow can kick!

2
- ○ That cat is bad!
- ○ That cat naps.
- ○ Is the cat on the mat?

3
- ○ The rat will run.
- ○ That rat runs fast!
- ○ The rat can hop.

4
- ○ Oh no! A frog is in my house!
- ○ A frog hops.
- ○ The frog is green.

5
- ○ The pot can get hot.
- ○ The pot is hot!
- ○ Fill the pot with mud.

Singular/Plural Nouns

 Many nouns, or naming words, add -s to show more than one.

Read each sentence. Draw a line under each naming word that means more than one.

1 I see hats and a cap.   **2** It sits on eggs.

3 The girls swim.   **4** Pam can pet cats.

Read each sentence. Write the naming word that means more than one.

_____
- -

5 The mugs are hot.   _____

_____
- -

6 Mud is on my hands.   _____

Singular/Plural Nouns

Many nouns, or naming words, add -s to show more than one.

Read the sets of sentences. Draw a line under the sentence that has a naming word that names more than one.

1 Jan has her mittens.

Jan has her mitten.

2 She will run up a hill.

She will run up hills.

3 Jan runs with her dogs.

Jan runs with her dog.

4 The dogs can jump.

The dog can jump.

Look at each picture. Read each word. Write the plural naming word that matches the picture.

5 _____

cat _____

6 _____

sock _____

Singular/Plural Nouns

Read each sentence. Fill in the circle next to the naming word that means more than one.

1 Jim gets mud on his hands.

- ◯ gets
- ◯ hands
- ◯ mud

2 Pam can fill the pots with mud.

- ◯ pots
- ◯ mud
- ◯ fill

3 The dogs dig fast.

- ◯ dig
- ◯ fast
- ◯ dogs

4 The ants are on the plant.

- ◯ ants
- ◯ plant
- ◯ are

5 The frogs hop.

- ◯ The
- ◯ frogs
- ◯ hop

Action Words

 An action word tells what happens.

Read each sentence. Circle the word that tells what happens.

1 **The hen sits.**   **2** **Mom sees the hen.**

3 **The dog digs.**   **4** **The cat naps.**

Read the words. Use the words to finish the sentences.

| sees | run |

5 She _____ eggs.

6 It can _____ fast.

Action Words

An action word tells what happens.

Look at the pictures. Read the action words in the box. Write the correct action word on the line.

talk
play
dance
run

1 Sue and Al ____play____ ball.

2 The bears _____ .

3 Rabbit and Pig _____ .

4 Tami and Lee _____ fast.

Scholastic Professional Books

Action Words

Read each sentence. Fill in the circle next to the action word.

1 **The hen sits.**
- ⬯ hen
- ⬯ sits
- ⬯ The

2 **The cat naps in the van.**
- ⬯ naps
- ⬯ cat
- ⬯ van

3 **The green frog hops.**
- ⬯ frog
- ⬯ green
- ⬯ hops

4 **The dog digs.**
- ⬯ digs
- ⬯ dog
- ⬯ The

5 **The big pig ran.**
- ⬯ big
- ⬯ pig
- ⬯ ran

Scholastic Professional Books

Naming Words

 A naming word names a person, place, or thing.

Read each sentence. Draw a line under the naming word.

1 We play at school.   **2** The ball is fast.

3 The girl kicks.   **4** The friends run.

Look at each box. Circle the naming word that belongs in that box.

Person	Place	Thing
girl	ball	Pam
school	Bill	man
ball	school	ball

Naming Words

 A naming word names a person, place, or thing.

Read each sentence. Circle each naming word. Draw a line to match the sentence to the picture of the naming word.

1 Run and kick in the park.

2 Kick with a foot.

3 Kick the ball.

4 The girl will run to get it.

5 Kick it to the net.

Naming Words

Read each sentence. Fill in the circle next to the word that names a person, place, or thing.

1 Let's play in the park.

◯ play

◯ Let's

◯ park

2 The girl can run and kick.

◯ girl

◯ run

◯ kick

3 Kick the ball.

◯ ball

◯ the

◯ kick

4 The friend can jump.

◯ can

◯ jump

◯ friend

5 Jump to the net.

◯ get

◯ net

◯ jump

Word Order

Words in a sentence must be in an order that makes sense.

Read each group of words. Circle the words that are in an order that makes sense. Draw a line under each capital letter.

1 The king is sad.

sad. king is The

2 bake Let's cake. him a

Let's bake him a cake.

3 the king Tell to come.

Tell the king to come.

4 Let's eat the cake.

eat Let's the cake.

Read the words. Write them in order.

king The eats .

_____

- -

_____

Word Order

Words in a sentence must be in an order that makes sense.

These words are mixed up. Put them in order.
Then write each sentence.

1 snow. bear likes This

_____

- -

_____

2 water cold. The is

_____

- -

_____

3 fast. The runs bear

_____

- -

_____

4 play. bears Two

_____

- -

_____

Scholastic Professional Books

Word Order

Read each group of words. Then fill in the circle next to the words that are in an order that makes sense.

1

- ◯ Pam will bake a cake.
- ◯ bake Pam a will cake.
- ◯ will Pam cake. a bake

2

- ◯ will king. the see Pam
- ◯ king. Pam see will the
- ◯ Pam will see the king.

3

- ◯ duck. The king has a
- ◯ The king has a duck.
- ◯ has a king The duck.

4

- ◯ lake. the in is The duck
- ◯ The duck is in the lake.
- ◯ The lake. duck in is the

5

- ◯ The king will eat cake.
- ◯ king will The cake. eat
- ◯ cake. king will The eat

Capitalizing Titles

Important words in a title are capitalized.

Circle all the words that are capitalized.

What to See at Night

The Light of the Moon

⭐ See Many Stars! ⭐

The Sun and the Moon

Now use some of the words from the titles above to write your own titles.

_____

- -

_____

_____

- -

_____

Scholastic Professional Books

Capitalizing Titles

Important words in a title are capitalized.

Read the titles. Circle all the words that should be capitalized.

1 look at the stars!

2 the moon shines at night

3 we see planets

4 many moons shine

5 night and day

Read each set of titles. Draw a line under the correct title.

6 The Sun in the Sky

the sun in the sky

7 See the stars!

See the Stars!

Capitalizing Titles

Read the titles. Fill in the circle next to the title with the correct words capitalized.

1

- ◯ **Where Is the Sun?**
- ◯ **Where is the sun?**
- ◯ **Where Is The Sun?**

2

- ◯ **many cats to see**
- ◯ **Many cats To See**
- ◯ **Many Cats to See**

3

- ◯ **Day and Night**
- ◯ **day And night**
- ◯ **Day And Night**

4

- ◯ **how many pigs?**
- ◯ **How Many Pigs?**
- ◯ **How many pigs?**

5

- ◯ **the Big Bad wolf**
- ◯ **the big, bad wolf**
- ◯ **The Big, Bad Wolf**

Naming Words

 A naming word names a person, place, or thing.

Read each sentence. Draw a line under the word or words that name the person, place, or thing in each sentence.

1 **The pot is big.** **2** **The pan is big.**

3 **See the top?** **4** **Jim can mop.**

Draw a line from each sentence to the picture that shows the naming word in that sentence.

5 **The pot is hot.**

6 **See the pan?**

7 **Jim is fast.**

Naming Words

A naming word names a person, place, or thing.

Circle the naming words in the sentences.

 Jan can go in a van.

2 The van can go fast.

3 The van is on a hill.

4 Dan sees Jan.

Draw a picture of a person, place, or thing.
Write a sentence about your picture.
Circle the naming word.

┌───┐
│   │
│   │
│   │
│   │
│   │
│   │
└───┘

_____

 _____

Scholastic Professional Books

Naming Words

Read each sentence. Fill in the circle next to the naming word.

1 **See the hot pans?**

- ⬭ hot
- ⬭ See
- ⬭ pans

2 **See Jim mop fast.**

- ⬭ fast
- ⬭ Jim
- ⬭ See

3 **The cat naps.**

- ⬭ cat
- ⬭ The
- ⬭ naps

4 **The rat hid.**

- ⬭ The
- ⬭ rat
- ⬭ hid

5 **Can the cat see?**

- ⬭ see
- ⬭ cat
- ⬭ Can

Linking Verbs

 Is, *are*, *was*, and *were* are linking verbs. *Is* tells about one. *Are* tells about more than one. *Was* tells about one in the past. *Were* tells about more than one in the past.

Read each sentence. Draw a line under the linking verb <u>is</u>, <u>are</u>, <u>was</u>, or <u>were</u>.

1 The hen is digging.

2 The chicks were helping.

3 The pig was having fun.

4 The cat and duck are playing.

Read each sentence. Circle <u>now</u> or <u>in the past</u> to show when it happens or happened.

5 The hen is planting.   now   in the past

6 The cat was not helping.   now   in the past

7 The chicks are with the hen.   now   in the past

Linking Verbs

Is, are, was, and were are linking verbs. Is tells about one. Are tells about more than one. Was tells about one in the past. Were tells about more than one in the past.

Circle the linking verb. Write now or past to tell when the action happens or happened.

1 The chicks are eating. _____

2 The duck is swimming. _____

3 The cat was napping. _____

4 The pig is digging. _____

5 They were playing. _____

Linking Verbs

Fill in the circle next to the linking verb that completes each sentence.

1 The hen ___ sitting.

- ◯ was
- ◯ are
- ◯ were

2 They ___ playing.

- ◯ were
- ◯ is
- ◯ was

3 The pigs ___ digging.

- ◯ was
- ◯ is
- ◯ are

4 The duck ___ swimming.

- ◯ were
- ◯ is
- ◯ are

5 The chicks ___ napping.

- ◯ was
- ◯ is
- ◯ are

Scholastic Professional Books

Capitalizing Names and First Words

 The first word in a sentence starts with a capital letter. Sometimes words that name a person, place, or thing begin with a capital letter.

Read the sentences. Circle the words that are capitalized.

1 **The goats Gruff have a problem.**

2 **They do not like the Troll.**

3 **His name is Nosey.**

4 **He is big and bad.**

Draw a line to match each sentence to why the underlined word is capitalized.

5 **Dan and <u>Pam</u> like the play.**

First word in a sentence.

6 **<u>They</u> will read it to Jim.**

Names a person, place, or thing.

Capitalizing Names

Sometimes the names of people, places, and things are special.
They begin with a capital letter.

Circle the special names in the picture. Write each one correctly on a line.

1 _____

2 _____

3 _____

4 _____

Capitalizing Names and First Words

Read each sentence. Fill in the circle next to the word that needs a capital letter.

1 i like the goats Gruff.

◯ Goats

◯ The

◯ I

2 I read the story with ron.

◯ Read

◯ Story

◯ Ron

3 Little gruff had a problem.

◯ Had

◯ Gruff

◯ Problem

4 troll was on the bridge.

◯ A

◯ Bridge

◯ Troll

5 His name was nosey.

◯ Name

◯ Nosey

◯ His

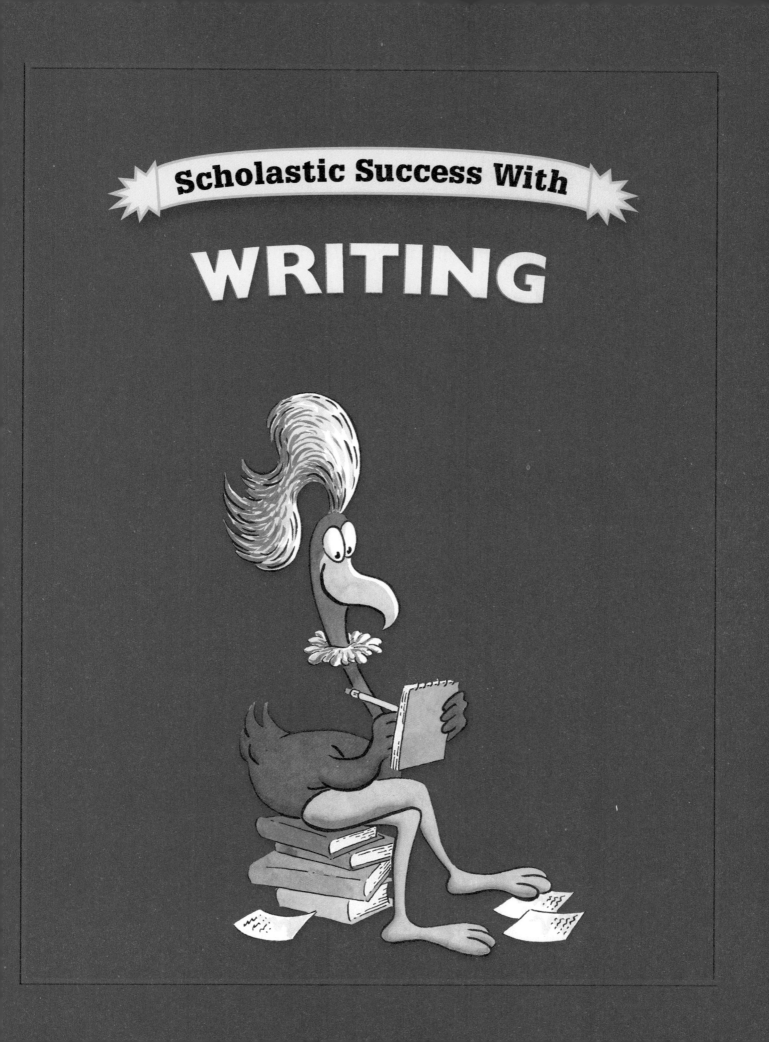

That's Amazing!

A sentence begins with a **capital letter**.

Help the mouse through the maze by coloring each box with a word that begins with a capital letter.

The	For	That	with	know	but
here	on	When	Have	next	we
as	after	good	Make	there	see
Go	Look	Are	Could	is	why
This	who	said	in	come	them
Has	Name	Before	Her	Where	The

 Read the back of a cereal box. How many capital letters did you find? Write the number next to the cheese.

Squeak!

Circle the words that show the correct way to begin each sentence.

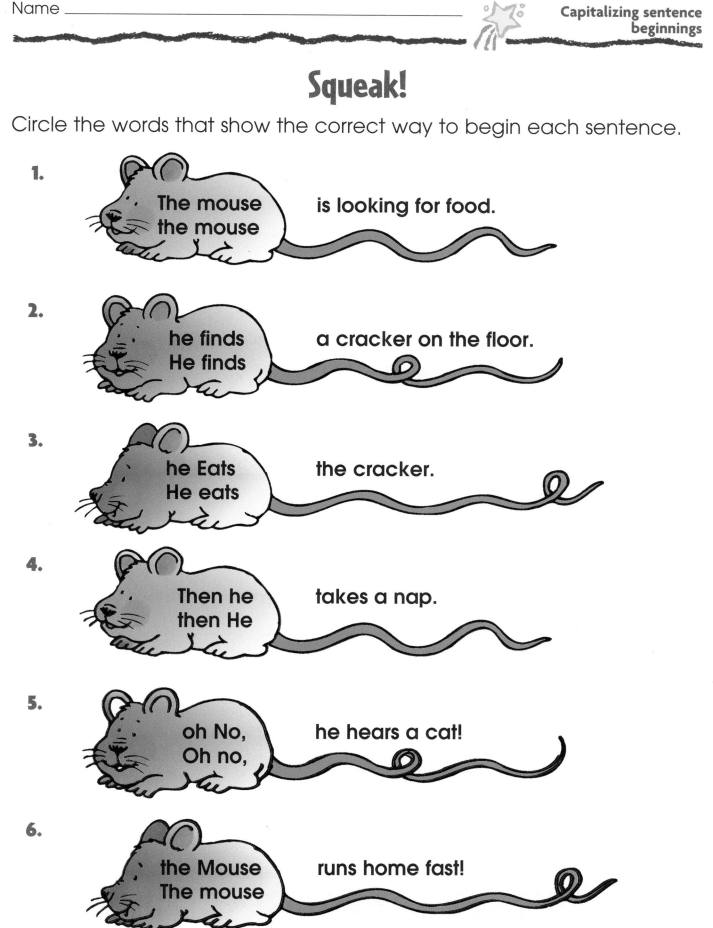

1. The mouse
the mouse
is looking for food.

2. he finds
He finds
a cracker on the floor.

3. he Eats
He eats
the cracker.

4. Then he
then He
takes a nap.

5. oh No,
Oh no,
he hears a cat!

6. the Mouse
The mouse
runs home fast!

Counting Sheep

Write the beginning words correctly to make a sentence.

1. we read _____ books before bed.

2. then we _____ hug good night.

3. my bed _____ is soft and cozy.

4. my cat _____ sleeps with me.

5. the sky _____ has turned dark.

6. my eyes _____ close.

On another piece of paper, copy a sentence from your favorite bedtime book. Circle the capital letter at the beginning.

Sweet Dreams!

Write each beginning word correctly to make a sentence.

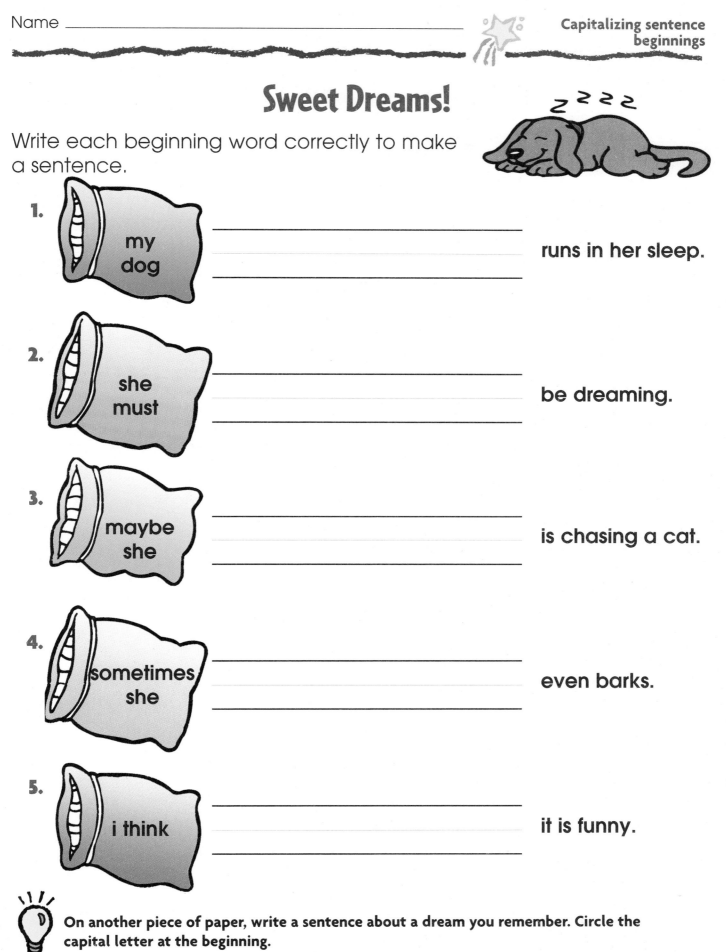

1. **my dog** _____ runs in her sleep.

2. **she must** _____ be dreaming.

3. **maybe she** _____ is chasing a cat.

4. **sometimes she** _____ even barks.

5. **i think** _____ it is funny.

On another piece of paper, write a sentence about a dream you remember. Circle the capital letter at the beginning.

The Night Sky

A **telling sentence** ends with a **period.**

period

Add a period to each sentence.

1. Many things shine in the sky at night____

2. The moon looks the brightest____

3. It is closest to Earth____

4. The stars look like tiny dots____

5. They are very far away____

6. The sun is a star____

7. Planets look like colored stars____

8. Their light does not twinkle____

9. Shooting stars look like stars that are falling____

10. There are many things to see in the night sky____

Scholastic Professional Books

Twinkle, Twinkle Little Star

Rewrite each sentence using periods.

1. Tonight I saw a star

_____

_____

2. I saw the star twinkle

_____

_____

3. It looked like a candle

_____

_____

4. It was very bright

_____

_____

5. I made a wish

_____

_____

6. I hope it comes true

_____

_____

Look for the brightest star in the sky. Make a wish. On another piece of paper, write a sentence about your wish.

Hop to It!

A **telling sentence** *begins with a* **capital letter** *and ends with a* **period**.

Rewrite each sentence correctly.

1. frogs and toads lay eggs

_____

_____

2. the eggs are in the water

_____

_____

3. tadpoles hatch from the eggs

_____

_____

4. the tadpoles grow legs

_____

_____

5. the tadpoles lose their tails

_____

_____

Hop to It Some More!

Rewrite each sentence correctly.

1. tadpoles become frogs or toads

_____

2. frogs live near water

_____

3. toads live mostly on dry land

_____

4. frogs have wet skin

_____

5. toads have bumpy skin

_____

On another piece of paper, write three sentences about a time that you saw a frog or toad. Make sure you use capital letters and periods correctly.

Patriotic Sentences

*A **sentence** tells a complete idea. It should always make sense.*

Color the flag to show:

RED = sentence   WHITE = not a sentence

★ ★ ★ ★ ★ ★ ★ ★ ★ ★ ★ ★ ★ ★ ★ ★ ★ ★ ★ ★ ★ ★ ★ ★ ★ ★ ★ ★ ★ ★ ★ ★ ★ ★ ★ ★ ★ ★ ★ ★ ★ ★ ★ ★ ★ ★ ★ ★ ★ ★	This is a flag.
	The flag
	The flag has stars.
	The stars
	The stars are white.
	The stripes
	The stripes are red.

And white

The stripes are white.

Blue part

The flag has a blue part.

There are

There are 50 stars.

💡 **Color the star part of the flag with a blue crayon. Then on another piece of paper, write a complete sentence about your colorful flag.**

High-Flying Sentences

Color each flag that tells a complete thought. Leave the other flags blank.

We made a flag.

The big flag

The flag is big.

Blue and purple

It is purple and blue.

I hung it in my room.

In my room

On another piece of paper, turn this into a sentence: The biggest flag.

At the Seashore

Unscramble the words to make a sentence. Write the new sentence below each picture. Finish each picture to match the sentence.

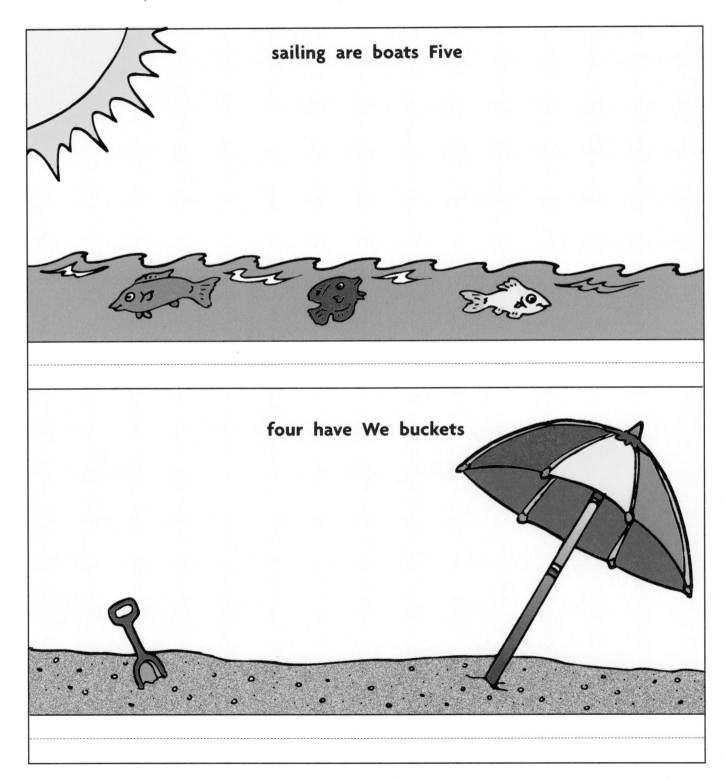

sailing are boats Five

four have We buckets

In the Rain Forest

Unscramble the words to make a sentence. Write the new sentence.
Do not forget to put a period at the end.

A hiding jaguar is

_____

- -

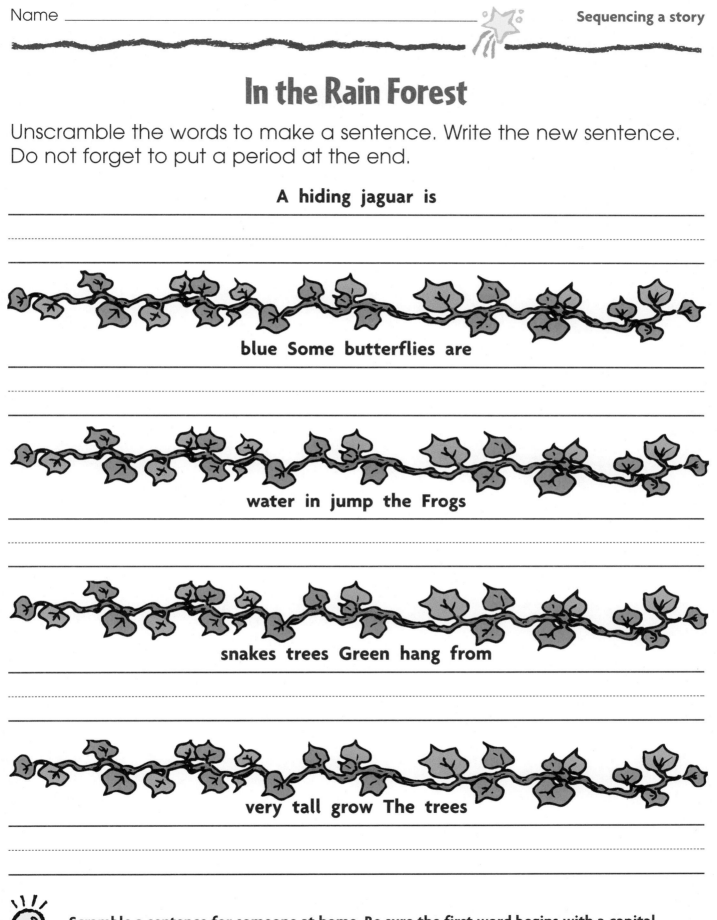

blue Some butterflies are

_____

- -

water in jump the Frogs

_____

- -

snakes trees Green hang from

_____

- -

very tall grow The trees

_____

- -

Scramble a sentence for someone at home. Be sure the first word begins with a capital.

Snakes Alive!

A *sentence has a* **naming part**. *It tells who or what the sentence is about.*

Color the snake that tells the naming part in each sentence below.

1. The phone   is ringing.

2. My dad   is the coach.

3. Jon's hamster   ran away.

4. Our bus   was late.

5. The teacher   left his home.

6. Greg and Pete   visit us.

On another piece of paper, write one of the sentences using a different naming part.

Slithering Sentences

Circle the naming part in each sentence below.
Then color the picture to match.

1. The blue snake is playing with a friend.

2. The yellow snake is climbing a tree.

3. The green snake hides under rocks.

4. The brown snake is swimming.

5. The red snake is hanging on a tree.

6. The purple snake sleeps in trees.

7. The black snake rests on a rock.

8. The orange snake is near an egg.

 Look around you. On another piece of paper, write three people or things that could be the naming part of a sentence.

Who Is That?

The naming part of a sentence can be a person.

Use the pictures to find naming parts to make each sentence complete.

_____

1. _____ fell on the ice.

_____

2. _____ won the race.

_____

3. _____ went inside the dark cave.

_____

4. _____ climbed the hill.

_____

5. _____ swam across the pool.

Scholastic Professional Books

Where Is That?

 The naming part of a sentence can be a place or a thing.

Use naming parts to complete each sentence that tells about the map.

Tree Lane

Park Road

1. _____ is near the swings.

2. _____ is far from the cave.

3. _____ is a good place to fish.

4. _____ has bats inside.

5. _____ is along Tree Lane.

Find the naming part of three sentences in your favorite book.

Family Photos

 The naming part of a sentence can be a person, a place, or a thing.

Use your own naming parts to write a complete sentence about each picture.

_____

- -

_____

- -

_____

_____

- -

_____

- -

_____

More Family Photos

Use your own naming parts to write a complete sentence about each picture.

_____

- -

_____

- -

_____

_____

- -

_____

- -

_____

Look at your family pictures. On another piece of paper, write a sentence telling about two of them.

No Bones About It!

A sentence has an **action part**. It tells what is happening.

Color the bone that tells the action part in each sentence below.

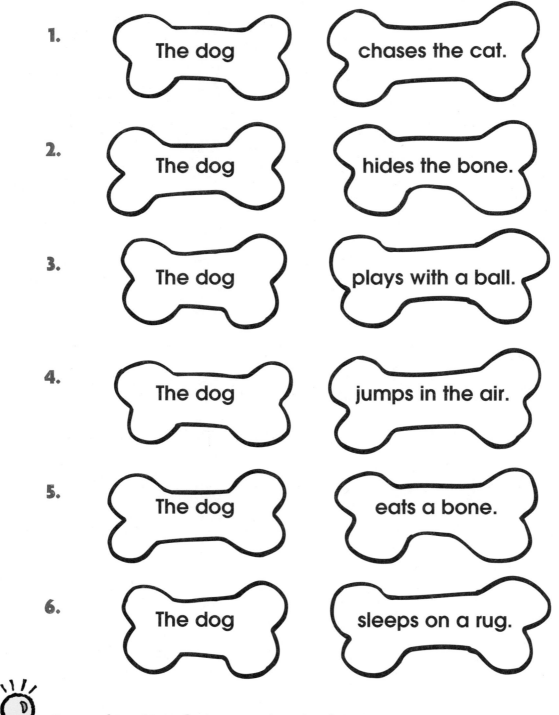

1. The dog   chases the cat.

2. The dog   hides the bone.

3. The dog   plays with a ball.

4. The dog   jumps in the air.

5. The dog   eats a bone.

6. The dog   sleeps on a rug.

On another piece of paper, rewrite your favorite sentence.

Mighty Good Sentences

Choose the ending that tells what each dog is doing. Remember to use periods.

is eating.

is sleeping.

is jumping.

is barking.

_____

1. The white dog _____

_____

2. The gray dog _____

_____

3. The spotted dog _____

_____

4. The striped dog _____

On another piece of paper, draw another dog and write a sentence about it.

A Busy Classroom

The action part of a sentence is called the **verb**.

Complete each sentence with an action verb to tell what is happening in the picture. Remember to use periods.

_____

1. Mr. Downs _____

_____

2. The fish _____

_____

3. James _____

_____

4. Cara _____

On another piece of paper, write a sentence about your teacher. Circle the action word.

Scholastic Professional Books

Pencil It In

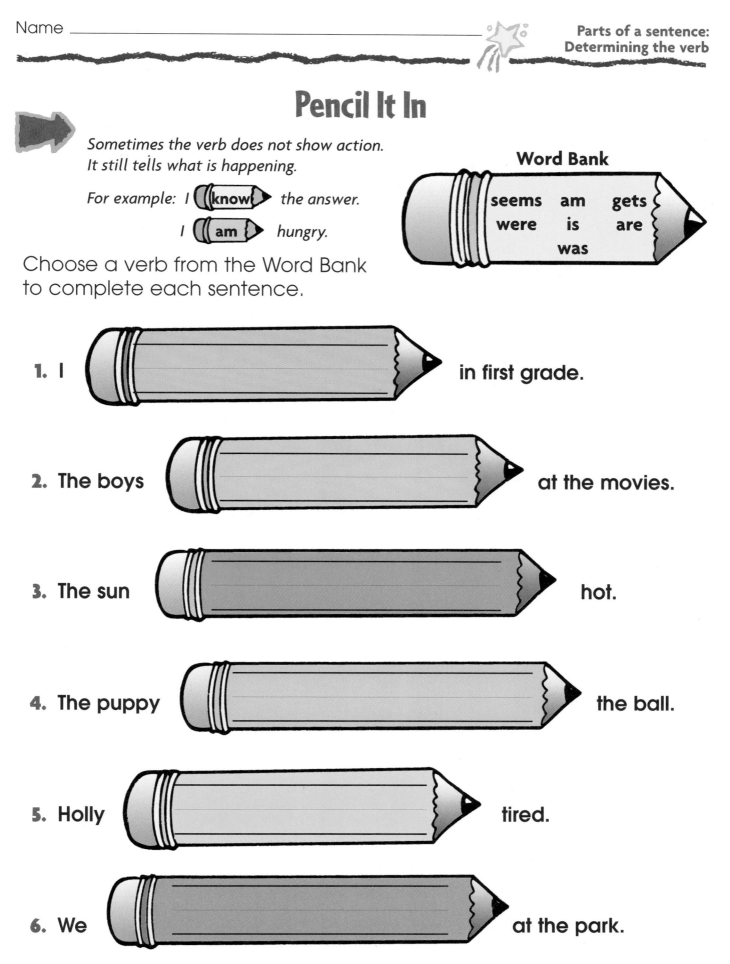

Sometimes the verb does not show action.
It still tells what is happening.

For example: I know the answer.
I am hungry.

Word Bank

seems   am   gets
were   is   are
was

Choose a verb from the Word Bank
to complete each sentence.

1. I _____ in first grade.

2. The boys _____ at the movies.

3. The sun _____ hot.

4. The puppy _____ the ball.

5. Holly _____ tired.

6. We _____ at the park.

Topsy-Turvy!

A sentence has a verb that tells what is happening.

Write five silly sentences that tell what is happening in the pictures.

_____

1. _____

_____

2. _____

_____

3. _____

_____

4. _____

_____

5. _____

What Is Going On?

Look around you. Write four sentences that tell what is happening.

_____

1. _____

_____

_____

_____

2. _____

_____

_____

_____

3. _____

_____

_____

_____

4. _____

_____

_____

_____

Find five action words in your favorite book. Write them on another piece of paper.

The Caboose

 A sentence is more interesting when it tells **where** *the action is happening.*

In each caboose, draw a picture to show where each sentence takes place.

1.

The plane flew into the clouds.

2.

The princess played in the castle.

3.

The boys fished in the lake.

Chugging Along

Write an ending for each sentence that tells where the action takes place.

naming part   the action   where

1. The monkey   swings

2. The ball   flew

3. Jenna's family   went

4. The pig   slept

5. The glass   fell

When Was That?

*A sentence may also tell **when** the action takes place.*

Circle the part that tells when in each sentence.

1. George Washington lived long ago.

2. The mail carrier was late yesterday.

3. The bear slept in winter.

4. We are going to the zoo today.

5. The leaves change in the fall.

6. I lost my tooth last night.

7. It rained all day.

8. The party starts at noon.

9. We got home yesterday.

10. We ate turkey on Thanksgiving Day.

11. The kitten was playing this morning.

12. Tomorrow I am going to my grandmother's house.

On another piece of paper, make a time line of your life. Use it to write two sentences that tell when.

My Busy Day

*Part of a sentence may tell **when** the action happened.*

Write the beginning part of each sentence to tell about your day.
Draw a picture to match each sentence.

this morning.

this afternoon.

tonight.

On another piece of paper, write four sentences and draw four pictures to tell about your best day ever.

Silly Sentences

A sentence may have three parts: a naming part, an action, and a part that tells where or when.

Complete each missing part to make silly sentences.

the naming part	the action	where or when
1. The monkey		on his head.
2. My dad	is hopping	
3.	flipped	in the forest.
4. The ball	bounced	
5. My shoes		at the pool.
6. The snake	twisted	
7. The bubbles	filled	

On another piece of paper, write a new sentence by scrambling three parts listed above. For example, use the naming part from #1, the action part from #2, and where or when from #3. Draw a picture of your sentence.

Sweet Sentences

Use choices from each part to make three "sweet" sentences.

naming part	action	where or when
I	ate doughnuts	at the bakery
She	ate candy	at the party
He	chewed gum	at the circus

 On another piece of paper, name the three parts of this sentence: The doughnut shop closed at noon.

Scholastic Professional Books

Home Sweet Home

Write three sentences about the picture. For example: The dog is sleeping outside.

1. _____

_____

_____

_____

2. _____

_____

_____

_____

3. _____

_____

_____

The Construction Crew

Write three sentences about the picture. Include three parts in each sentence.

1. _____

_____

_____

2. _____

_____

_____

3. _____

_____

_____

Scholastic Professional Books

Mystery Boxes

Describing words help you imagine how something looks, feels, smells, sounds, or tastes.

Read the describing words to guess the mystery object. Use the Word Bank to help you.

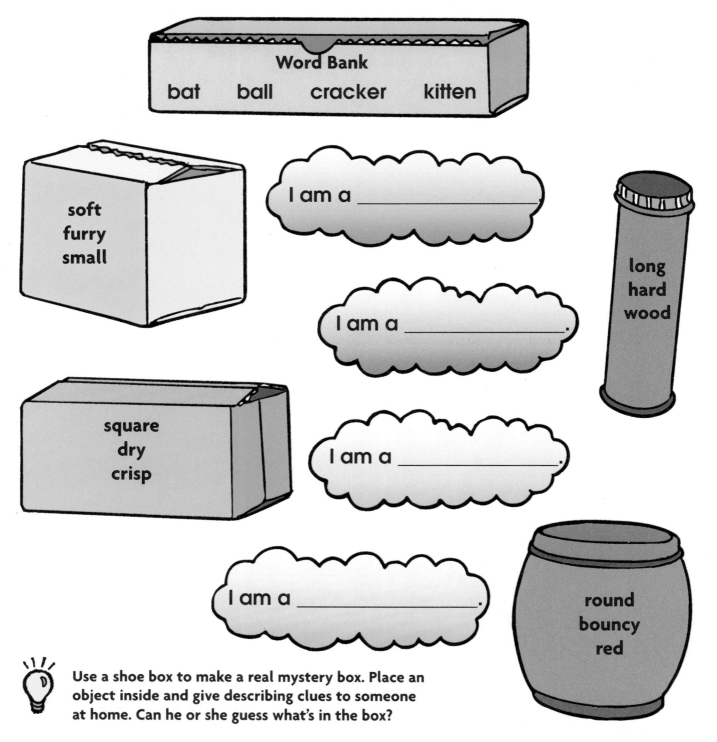

Word Bank

bat   ball   cracker   kitten

soft
furry
small

I am a _____

long
hard
wood

I am a _____.

square
dry
crisp

I am a _____.

I am a _____.

round
bouncy
red

Use a shoe box to make a real mystery box. Place an object inside and give describing clues to someone at home. Can he or she guess what's in the box?

Sensational Words

Choose words from the Word Bank to describe each picture.

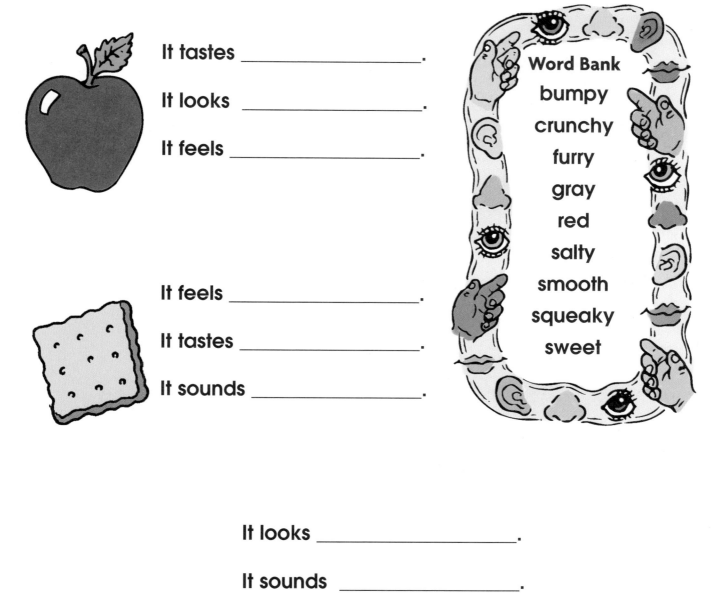

It tastes _____.

It looks _____.

It feels _____.

Word Bank

bumpy

crunchy

furry

gray

red

salty

smooth

squeaky

sweet

It feels _____.

It tastes _____.

It sounds _____.

It looks _____.

It sounds _____.

It feels _____.

 Find two objects outside. On another piece of paper, write two adjectives to describe each object.

Pretty Packages

The describing words in a sentence help the reader paint a picture in his or her mind.

Write three words to describe each gift. Then color them to match.

_____ (color)

_____ (color)

_____ (pattern)

_____ (color)

_____ (color)

_____ (pattern)

_____ (color)

_____ (color)

_____ (pattern)

_____ (color)

_____ (color)

_____ (pattern)

💡 **Describe a "mystery object" to a friend. Can he or she guess what you are describing?**

What's Inside?

Use the describing words from page 244 to write a sentence about each package. For example: I found a swimsuit in the **yellow square** box.

1. I found _____ in the

_____

_____ package.

2. I found _____

_____ in the

_____ package.

3. I found _____ in the

_____

_____ package.

4. I found _____

_____ in the

_____ package.

A Walk in the Park

Describing words make a sentence more interesting.

Write describing words to finish each sentence.

1. A _____ duck is

   _____

   swimming in the _____ pond.

2. A _____ man is walking

   _____

   his _____ dog.

3. A _____ girl is

   _____

   flying a _____ kite.

4. A _____ woman is sitting

   _____

   on a _____ .

On another piece of paper, draw a picture of your favorite animal at the zoo. Then write two words to describe this animal.

Around Town

Write a sentence for each picture. Use the describing word in
the sentence.

large

_____
_____
_____
_____
_____

beautiful

_____
_____
_____
_____
_____

crowded

_____
_____
_____
_____
_____

noisy

_____
_____
_____
_____
_____

 On another piece of paper, write five words that describe your street.

Name _____

Keep It in Order

Sentences can be written in order to tell a story.

Finish each story by writing sentences about the last pictures.

1. First, the spider crawls up

Next, _____

Last, _____

2. First, there is a tadpole

Next, _____

Last, _____

What's Next?

Sentences can be written in order to give directions.

Finish each set of directions by writing sentences about the last pictures.

1. **First,** mix all the ingredients.

   _____

   Next, _____

   _____

   Last, _____

2. **First,** put your dog in the tub

   _____

   Next, _____

   _____

   Last, _____

Scholastic Professional Books

Which Title Fits?

The name of a story is called the **title**. *It matches with the story. Most of the words in a title begin with capital letters.*

Match each title with its story. Write the title above the picture.

A Big Beak	The Big Win
My Space Friend	A Knight's Tale

_____ (title)

_____ (title)

_____ (title)

_____ (title)

Scholastic Professional Books

A Terrific Title

Fill in the missing words to make your own story. Then write a title that fits with your story. Draw a picture about your story in the box.

_____
(title)

One _____ day,

_____ took his pet

_____ for a walk. First,

they went to the _____.

Then they walked to _____'s

house. Last, they went home to _____

_____. It was a

_____ day!

Story Strips

 A story has a beginning, middle, and end.

Write a sentence to tell about each part of the story. Remember to give the story a title.

Beginning

_____ (title)

_____

Middle

_____

End

_____

More Story Strips

 A story has a beginning, middle, and end.

Think of a story you know well. Write about the beginning, middle, and end parts. Draw pictures to match. Be sure to give your story a title.

_____
(title)

Beginning

_____
_ _

Middle

_____
_ _

End

_____
_ _

 Fold a piece of paper two times to make a storybook. Write a story and draw pictures to match. Do not forget to write a title for your story.

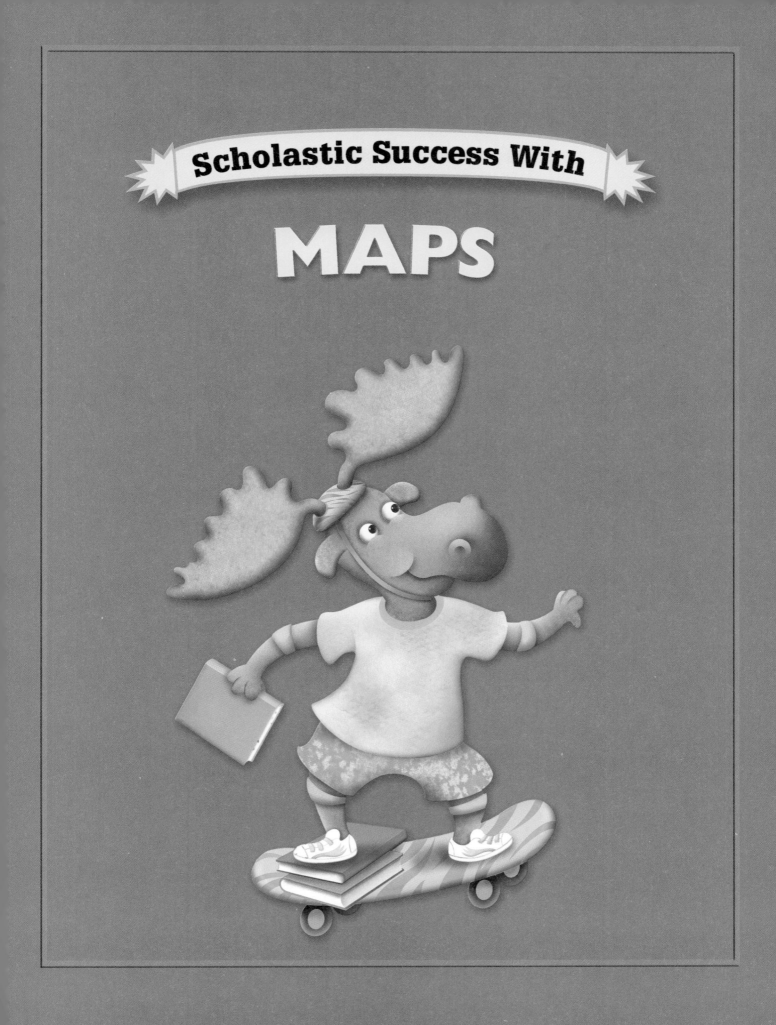

Scholastic Success With

MAPS

Places in Pictures

Pretend you are on
cloud in the sky.
You look down.
You take a photo.
Here it is!

Circle **YES** if you see the thing in the photo.
Circle **NO** if you do not.

1. house   **YES**   NO

2. street   **YES**   NO

3. tree   **YES**   NO

4. pond   **YES**   NO

5. What else do you see? _____

Scholastic Professional Books

You can show a place on a map.
A map is a drawing of a place from above.
This map shows the same place that the photo does.

6. Find a street on the photo.
   Then find the same street on the map.
   Write the name of the street. _____

7. The trees on the map are not colored.
   Color them green.

8. Find a swimming pool in the photo.
   Draw it in the same place on the map.

Making a Map

This picture shows a toy store.

1. Color the kite yellow.

2. Color the rug green.

3. Color the wagon red.

4. What is next to the drum? _____

5. Can you buy a teddy bear here? _____

This map shows the same toy store.
You can help draw the map.

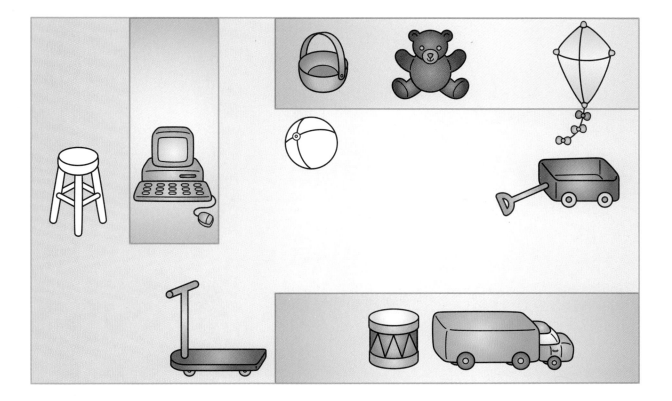

6. Find the ball in the picture.
   Make it the same color on the map.

7. Find the stool in the picture.
   Make it the same color on the map.

8. Find the rug in the picture.
   Draw it on the map in the same place.

Map Words

Many map words tell where things are.

The bird is **near** the branch.

The bird is **far** from the branch.

The bird is to the **left** of the bird house.

The bird is to the **right** of the bird house.

The bird is **above** the bath.

The bird is **below** the bath.

Write a word to complete each sentence.

near   far   left   right   above

1. The bird is _____ from the bird house.

2. The girl is _____ the bird house.

3. The bird is _____ the grass.

4. The bird house is to the _____ of the girl.

5. The path is to the _____ of the girl.

Big and Small Spaces

Maps can show big spaces or small spaces.

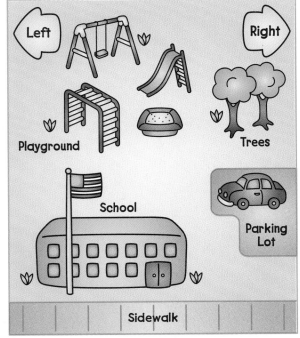

Map 1: This map shows a school playground.

Map 2: This map shows all of the school grounds.

Circle **YES** if the sentence is true.
Circle **NO** if the sentence is not true.

1. **The school is bigger than the trees.**   YES NO

2. **The playground is bigger than the parking lot.** YES NO

3. **The school is to the right of the playground.**   YES NO

4. **The trees are to the right of the playground.**   YES NO

Scholastic Professional Books

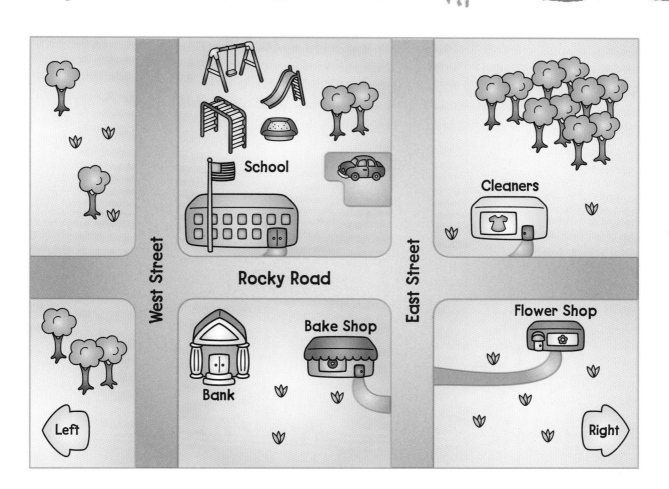

Map 3: This map shows three streets. Can you find the school?

5. What is the biggest
   building on this map? _____

6. What is the smallest
   building on this map? _____

7. Look at all three maps.
   Which map shows the biggest space? _____

8. Which map shows the smallest space? _____

Looking at Earth

If you were in outer space, you could see Earth. It would look like this.

1. **What shape is Earth?** _____

2. **Who lives on Earth?** _____

3. **Draw something that is the same shape as Earth.**

Scholastic Professional Books

A Globe

A globe is a model of Earth.
It is the same shape as Earth.

1. What colors do you see on the globe?

_____

2. What color stands for water?

_____

3. Is a globe smaller or bigger than Earth?

_____

Directions

Earth has four main **directions**.
They are north, south, east, and west.

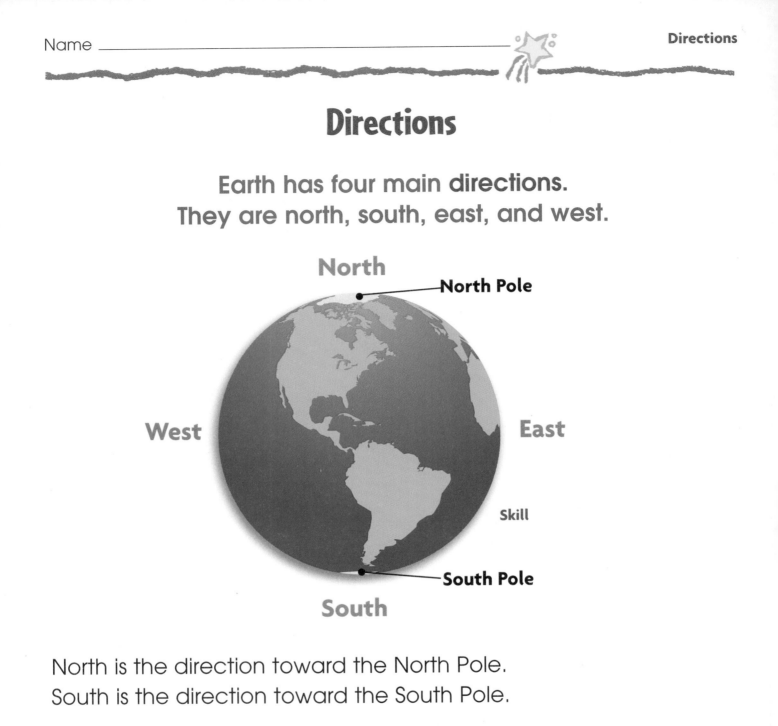

North is the direction toward the North Pole.
South is the direction toward the South Pole.

Can you find east and west on the picture, too?

1. What direction is the opposite of north? _____

2. What direction is the opposite of west? _____

Directions help you find places on a map.
This map shows a camp.
Point to the four directions.

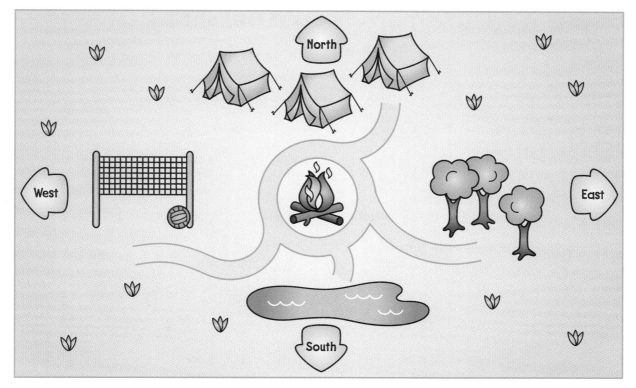

Where is each thing?
Write a direction word to describe it.

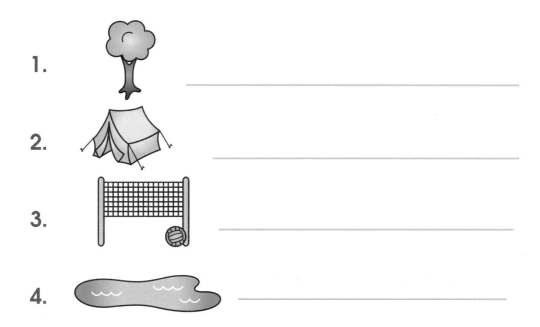

1. _____

2. _____

3. _____

4. _____

Using Directions

Directions tell you which way to go.
This map shows a pet shop.

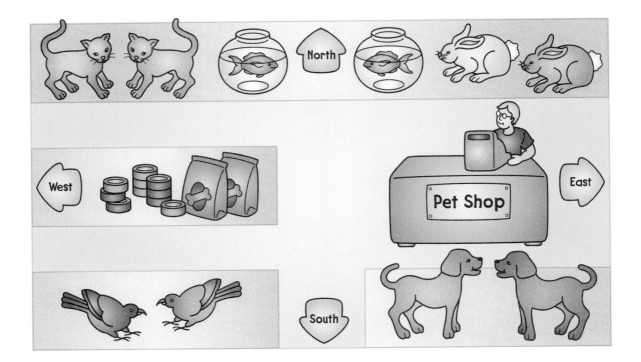

Write the direction word that tells how to get there.

1. from 🐦 to 🐱 _____

2. from 🐟 to 🐰 _____

3. from 🐕 to Pet Shop _____

4. from Pet Shop to _____

Come to the fair! You can have fun.

Draw a line to show where you go.

1. Start at the gate. Go north to the . Mmmm!

2. Now go west. Stop and ride on the .

3. Walk to the east. Get your face painted like a .

4. From here, go west and
   then north. Stop and play at the .

5. In which direction is the gate from the ?

Symbols

A symbol is a drawing that stands for something real.

The photo shows a road.   This is a symbol for a road.

Draw a line to match each photo to the correct symbol.

1.

2.

3.

4.

a.

b.

c.

d.

Here are some more symbols.

Draw the correct symbol next to each photo.

1.

2.

3.

4.

Symbols on Maps

Most maps have symbols.
A map key tells what each symbol stands for.

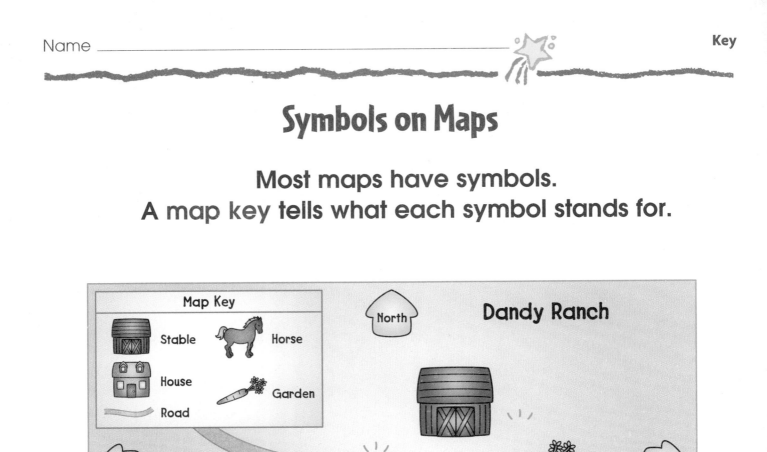

Use the map key.
Write what each symbol stands for.

1. _____

2. _____

3. _____

4. _____

The ranch has one new animal.

Circle the new animal on the map.
Use the map key to answer the questions.

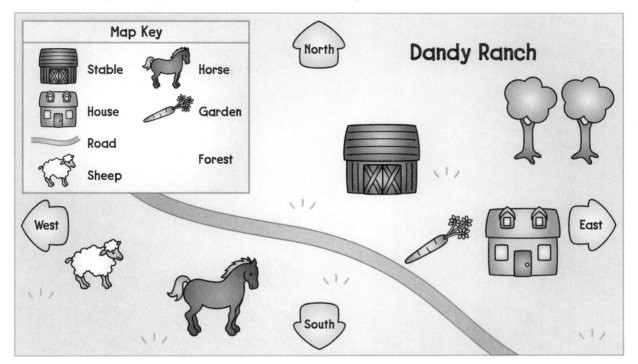

1. Is the horse north or south of the road? _____

2. What does 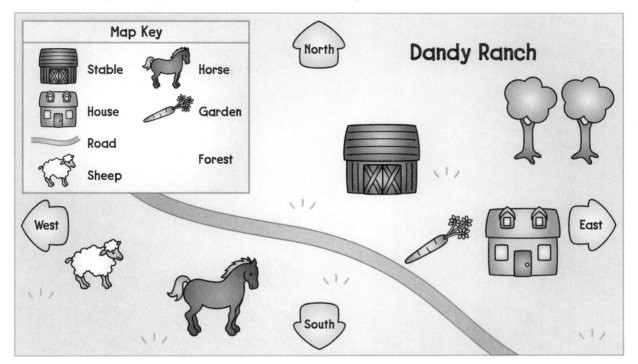 mean? _____

3. Is the garden east or west of the house? _____

4. Find the forest on the map.
   Add a tree symbol to the map key.

Scholastic Professional Books

Land and Water

Earth has different kinds of land.

Some land is flat.
A **plain** is flat land.

Some land is very high. A
mountain is very high land.

Some land is higher than
a plain but not as high as
a mountain. This land is
called a **hill**.

1. **What is the highest kind of land?**

   _____

2. **What is the flattest land?**

   _____

3. **Which is higher, a hill or a plain?**

   _____

Scholastic Professional Books

Earth has lots of water.

Some water runs across the land. This water is called a **river.**

Some water has land all around it. This water is called a **lake**.

These symbols stand for different kinds of land and water. Write a word to tell what each symbol stands for.

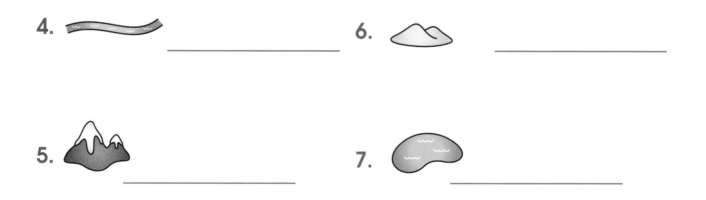

4. _____

6. _____

5. _____

7. _____

A Land and Water Map

This picture shows different kinds of land and water.

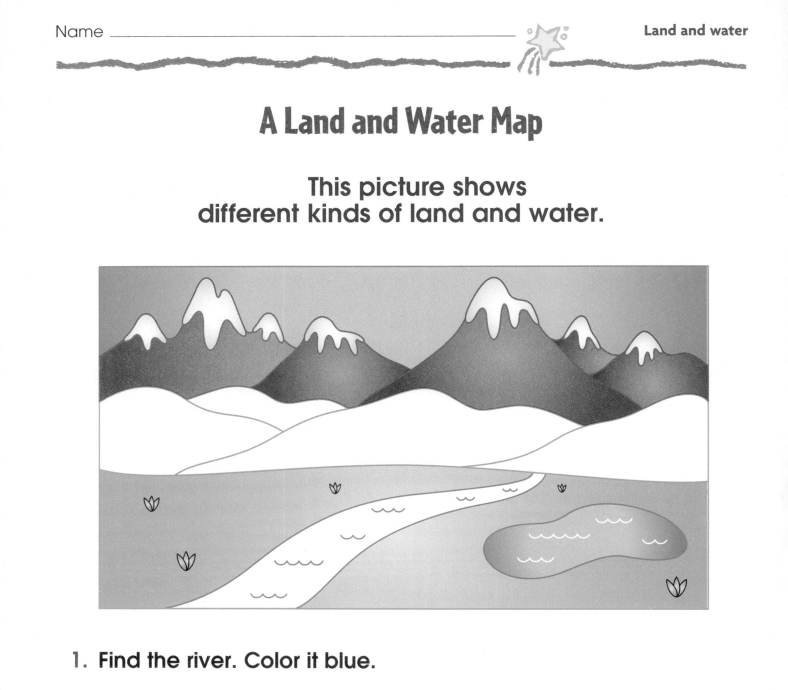

1. Find the river. Color it blue.

2. Find a body of water with land all around it.
   Write "lake" on it.

3. Find the hills. Color them light green.

4. Find the flat land. Write "plain" on it.

This map shows land and water, too.

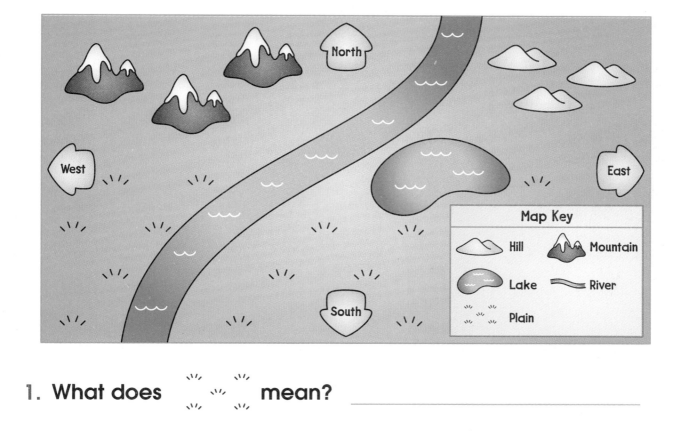

1. What does [image] mean? _____

2. Is the lake to the east or west of the river? _____

3. Are the mountains to the
   east or west of the hills? _____

4. Write a place where you can do each thing.

   climb _____ run _____

   swim _____ fish _____

A Park Map

This map shows a big park.
A park can have different kinds of land and water.

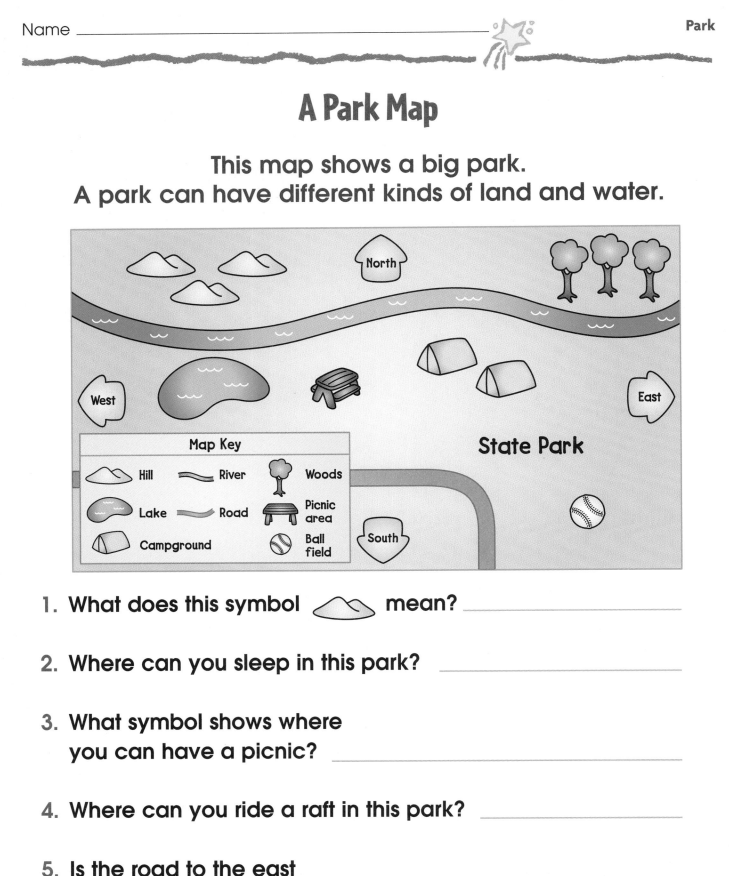

1. What does this symbol 🏔 mean? _____

2. Where can you sleep in this park? _____

3. What symbol shows where
   you can have a picnic? _____

4. Where can you ride a raft in this park? _____

5. Is the road to the east
   or west of the ball field? _____

This map shows a city park.

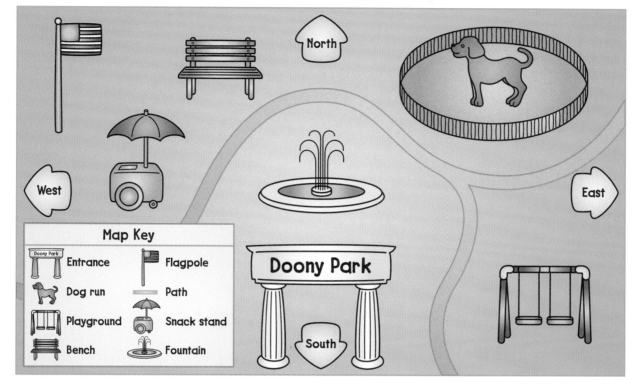

1. **What is the name of this park?**
   _____

2. **Where can you get something to eat?**
   _____

3. **What is north of the entrance?**
   _____

4. **Where can your dog play in this park?**
   _____

5. **Where can you ride a swing?**
   _____

6. **In which direction would you walk from the** 🌊 **to the** ☂️ _____

A Neighborhood Map

A map can show a neighborhood.

A neighborhood is a place where people live, work, and play. The people who live in a neighborhood are neighbors.

These pictures show different parts of Dale's neighborhood. Write a word for each picture.

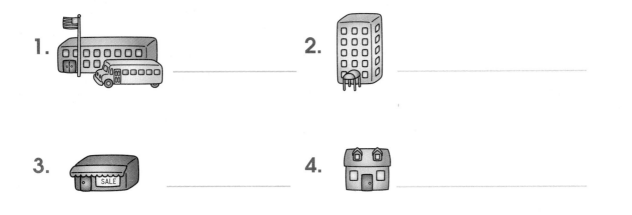

1. _____

2. _____

3. _____

4. _____

5. **Draw a picture of something in your neighborhood.**

Scholastic Professional Books

This map shows the neighborhood where Dale lives.

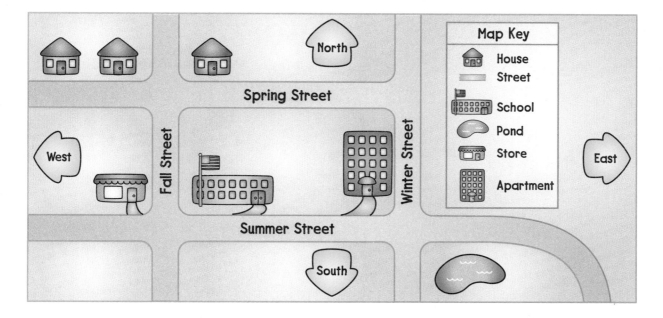

1. What does the symbol

 stand for? _____

2. Find the symbol for house.
   On what street are the houses? _____

3. Dale lives in an apartment.
   On what street does Dale live? _____

4. Dale is going to the store
   with her father. In which direction
   is the store from her home? _____

Going Places

Hari's family just moved to Wonder Town.
Use this map to help them get around.

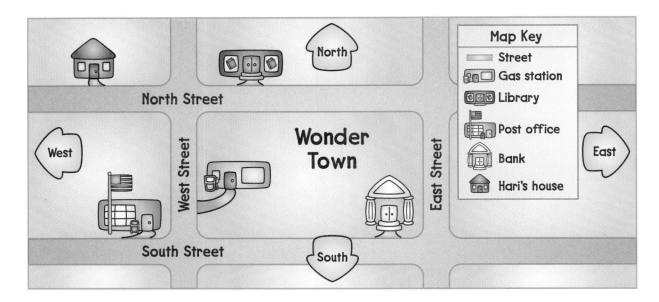

Tell Hari's family the street for each place.

1. **Hari's mother is going
   to the bank. It is on** _____.

2. **Hari's father is going
   to the gas station. It is on** _____.

3. **Hari's big brother is going
   to the library. It is on** _____.

4. **Hari's grandma is going
   to the post office. It is on** _____.

Scholastic Professional Books

Hari goes to school the same way each day. He follows a route. A **route** is a way to go from one place to another.

1. **Start at Hari's house.**
   Draw a line to show the route he can take to school.

2. **On what street is the school?** _____

3. **Omar is Hari's new friend.**
   Draw a line to show Omar's route to school.

4. **Does Omar live east or**
   west of the school? _____

5. **Is the library north or**
   south of the gas station? _____

Borders

Maps show where places begin and end.
A dividing line between two places is called a border.

Look at the fence in this photo. The fence shows where the border is.

Look at the line with dashes on this map. This line is a symbol. It stands for a border.

Maps show other kinds of borders, too. A river can be a border. So can a road. Draw an X on three kinds of borders on this map.

Scholastic Professional Books

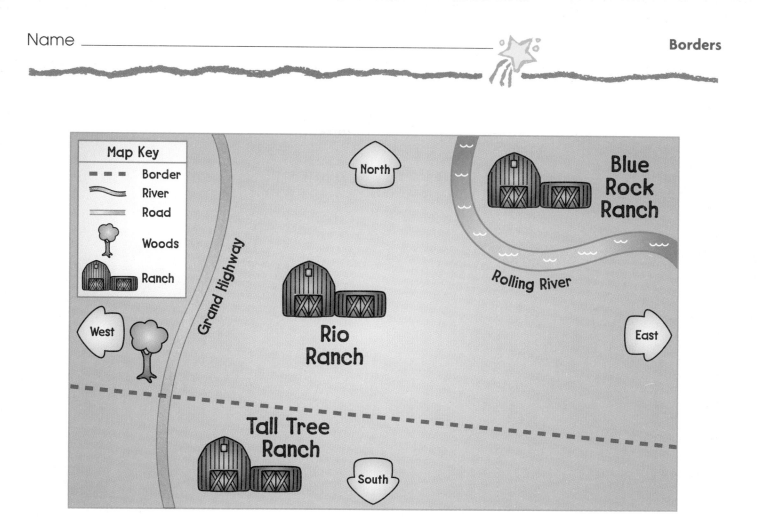

This map shows different borders.

1. This symbol – – – – – stands for a _____.

2. The border to the west of
   Rio Ranch is a _____.

3. What is the border between
   Rio Ranch and Blue Rock Ranch? _____

4. In which direction is Tall Tree Ranch
   from Rio Ranch? _____

5. Are the woods east or
   west of Rio Ranch? _____

The United States

Here is a map of the United States.

The United States is a large **country**.
A country is a land and people who live there.

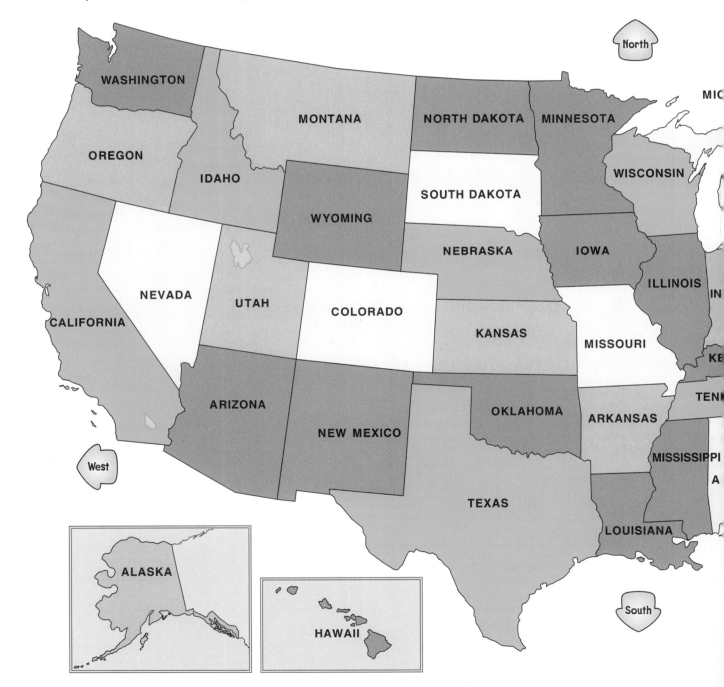

The United States has 50 states.
Each state is a part of the country.
The states are different shapes and sizes.

MAINE
VERMONT
NEW HAMPSHIRE
MASSACHUSETTS
NEW YORK
RHODE ISLAND
CONNECTICUT
PENNSYLVANIA
NEW JERSEY
DELAWARE
WEST VIRGINIA
MARYLAND
VIRGINIA
WASHINGTON, D.C.
NORTH CAROLINA
SOUTH CAROLINA
East
FLORIDA

MAP KEY
—— State border
✪ National capital

1. What does this symbol ——— mean?

_____

2. What is your state?

_____

3. How many states share a border with your state?

_____

4. Name a state in the east.

_____

5. Is Texas in the north or south?

_____

6. Is Oregon in the west or east?

_____

7. What state is south of Utah?

_____

8. What state is west of Ohio?

_____

A State Map

This map shows the state of Indiana. Each state has a capital city.

A capital is the city where the leaders of the state work. The capital of Indiana is Indianapolis.

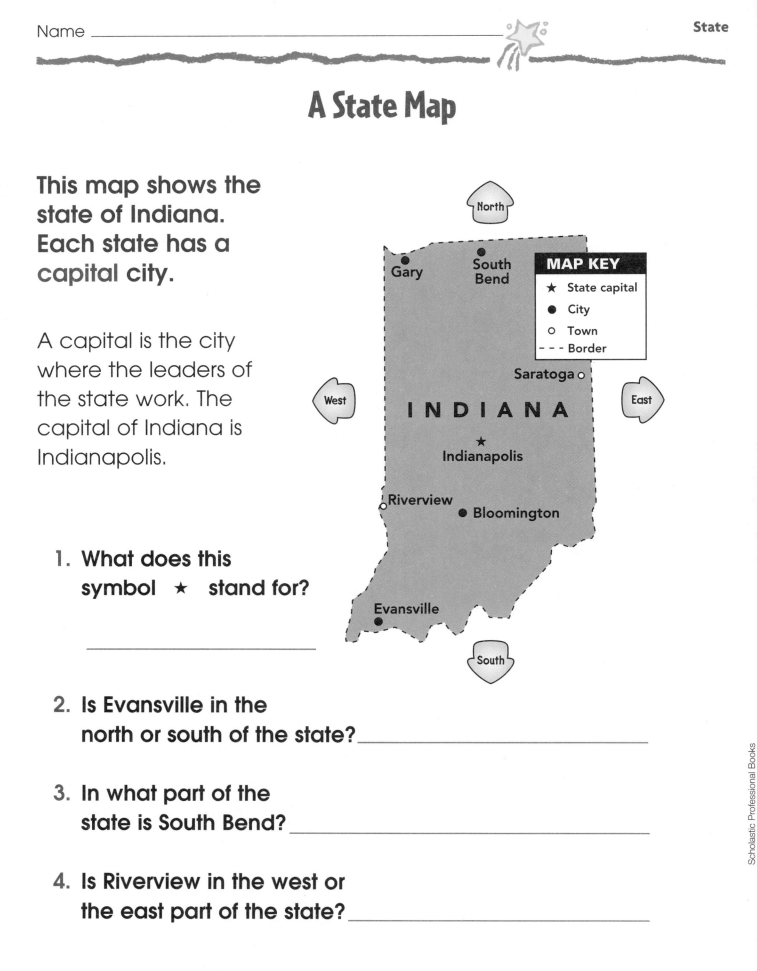

1. What does this symbol ★ stand for?

   _____

2. Is Evansville in the north or south of the state?_____

3. In what part of the state is South Bend? _____

4. Is Riverview in the west or the east part of the state?_____

This map shows where Indiana is in the United States.

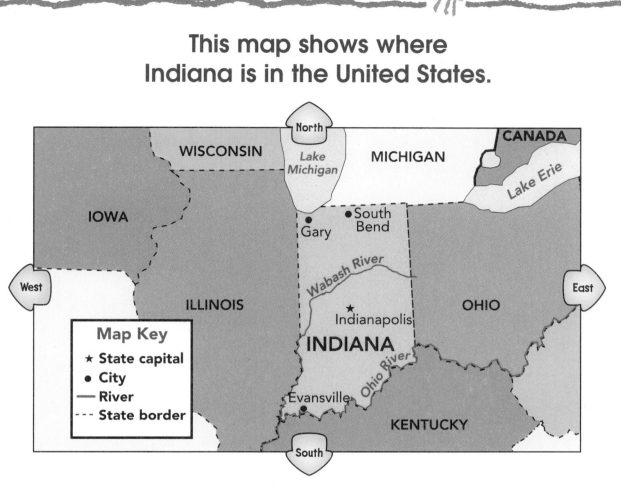

1. What does this symbol - - - - - - - - mean? _____

2. What river forms a border
   on the south of Indiana? _____

3. What river forms a border
   on the west of Indiana? _____

4. How many states share
   a border with Indiana? _____

5. What lake forms a border
   on the north of Indiana? _____

A City Map

The United States has a capital city.

It is Washington, D.C. The President of the United States lives and works there. So do other leaders of the country.

The President lives and works in the White House.

Washington, D.C., has many important buildings. You can see some of them on the map on page 291.

1. **Find the Washington Monument.**
   Is it north or south of the White House? _____

2. **Find the U.S. Capitol.**
   Trace a route on the map to the White House.

3. **Find the National Gallery of Art.**
   Is it east or west of the U.S. Capitol? _____

4. **Constitution Avenue runs from west to** _____ .

5. **Name a museum you would like to visit.**

_____

North

Washington, D.C.

White House

Pennsylvania Avenue

West

East

Constitution Avenue

National Gallery of Art

Museum of American History

National History Museum

U.S. Capitol

Washington Monument

Smithsonian

National Air and Space Museum

South

This is the Washington Monument.
It honors George Washington.
He was our first President.

This is the United States Capitol. Our country's leaders meet here.

North America

This map shows North America. North America is a continent.

A continent is a large body of land.
The United States is in North America.

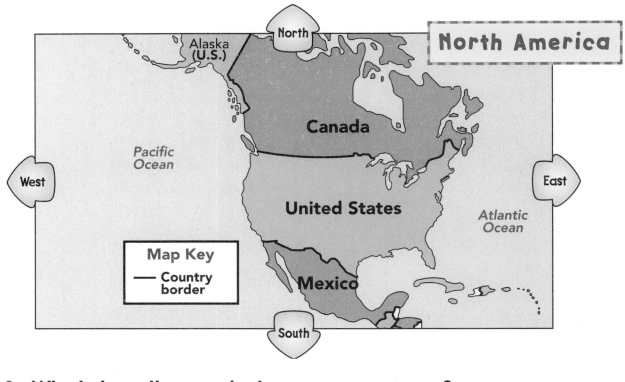

1. What does the symbol ——— mean?_____

2. What country is north
   of the United States? _____

3. In which direction is Mexico
   from the United States? _____

Around the continents are Earth's oceans.
An ocean is a very big body of salt water.

Earth has five oceans.
This map shows two of them.

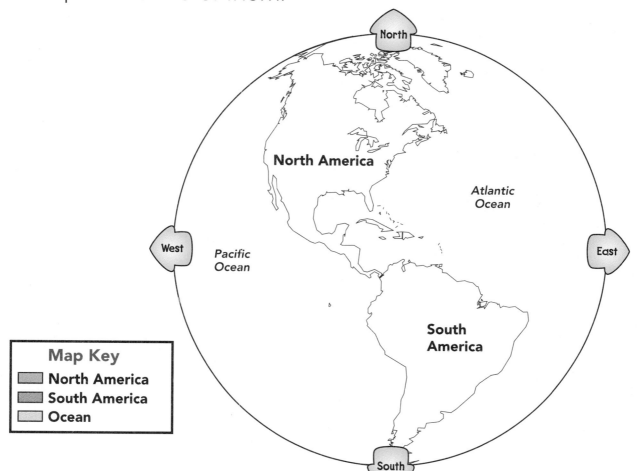

Map Key
North America
South America
Ocean

1. What ocean is to the
   east of North America? _____

2. What ocean is to the
   west of North America? _____

3. Color the map to match the map key.

A World Map

Remember, Earth
is round like a ball. But
you can only see one
side of a ball at once.

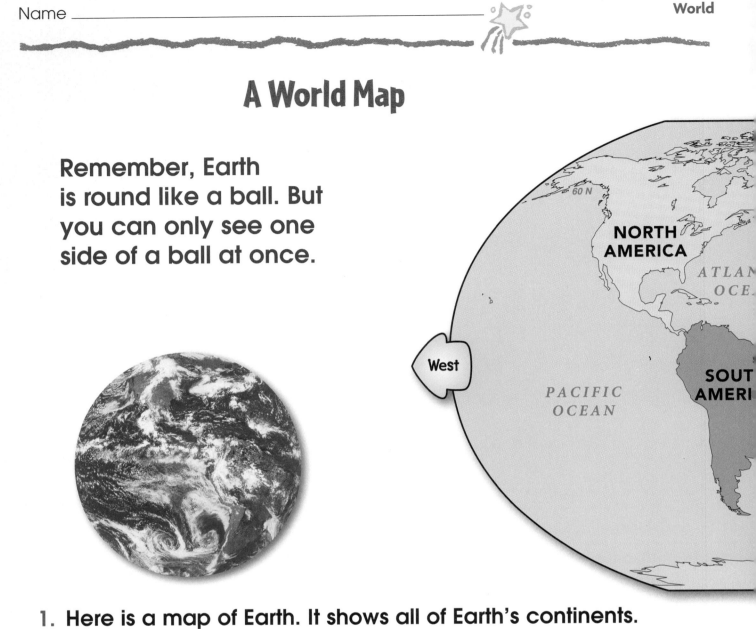

1. Here is a map of Earth. It shows all of Earth's continents.
   Count to find seven continents.

2. The map shows the five oceans of
   Earth, too. What are their names? _____

   _____   _____

   _____   _____

3. Which continent is north of Africa? _____

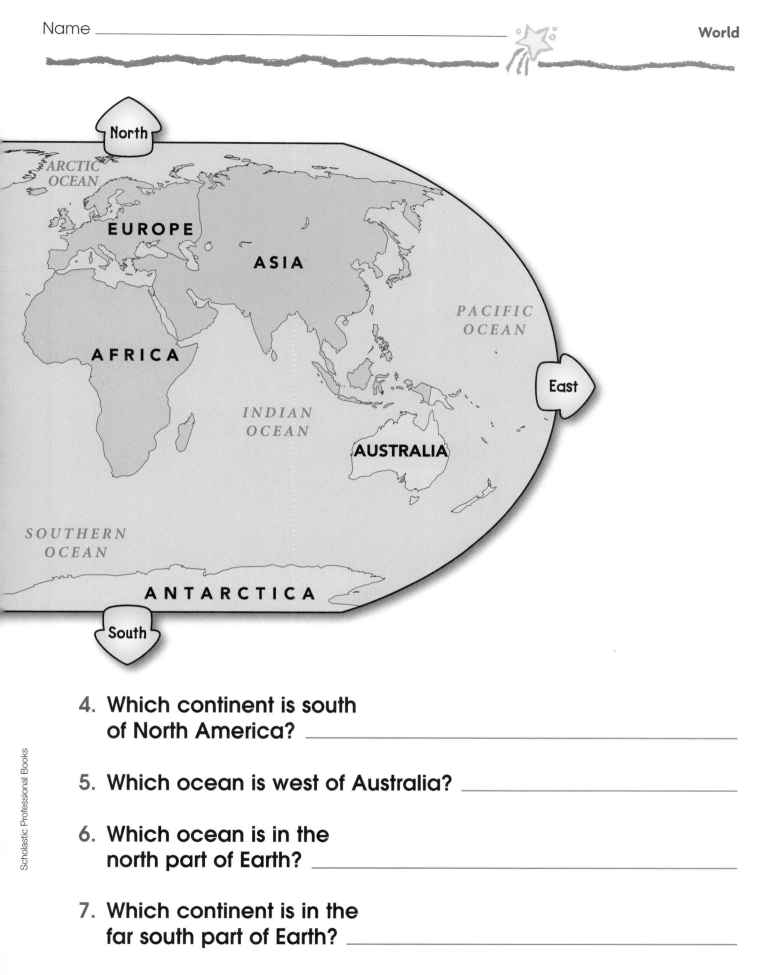

4. Which continent is south of North America? _____

5. Which ocean is west of Australia? _____

6. Which ocean is in the north part of Earth? _____

7. Which continent is in the far south part of Earth? _____

Map Review 1

Use the map to answer the questions.

Map Key

- ▭ Street
- 🚗 Gas station
- 📖 Library
- 🏛 Post office
- 🏦 Bank
- 🏠 Hari's house
- 🏠 Omar's house
- 🏫 School
- 〰 Pond
- ⛰ Hill

North Street

West Street

Wonder Town

East Street

South Street

North

West

East

South

1. What does this symbol ⬭ mean? _____

2. What kind of land is to the east of the bank? _____

3. On what street does Hari live? _____

4. Draw a route from Hari's house to Omar's house.

5. Where can Hari mail a letter? _____

6. Is Hari's house north or south of the school? _____

Map Review 2

Use the map to answer the questions.

Map Key
- ★ State capital
- --- State border
- Mountains
- Plains
- Hills

North

VIRGINIA

TENNESSEE

West

★Raleigh

NORTH
CAROLINA

East

Atlantic
Ocean

GEORGIA

SOUTH
CAROLINA

South

1. North Carolina is one of 50 _____ .

2. The capital of North Carolina is _____ .

3. This symbol [   ] means _____ .

4. North Carolina shares a border with _____ other states.

5. To the east of North Carolina is the _____ .

6. Are the mountains in the east or west part of North Carolina? _____

Thinking About Maps

You have learned a lot about maps. Use what you know to find the secret words.

1. The direction that is opposite of north.

   ___ ___ ___ ___ ___
    7   4

2. A body of water with land all around it.

   ___ ___ ___ ___ ___ ___
        9   5

3. A dividing line between two places.

   ___ ___ ___ ___ ___ ___
            6

4. A drawing that stands for something real.

   ___ ___ ___ ___ ___
    12

5. Very high land.

   ___ ___ ___ ___ ___ ___ ___
          1   8   3   2

6. A way to go from one place to another.

   ___ ___ ___ ___ ___ ___
          10 11

Now, can you figure out the secret words?

___ ___ ___ ___ ___ ___ ___ ___ ___ ___ ___ ___
1 2 3 4 5 6   7 8 9 10 11 12

Glossary

border	A border is a dividing line between two places.
capital	A capital is a city where government leaders work.
continent	A continent is a large body of land. North America is a continent.
country	A country is a land where people live.
direction	A direction tells where something is. The four main directions are north, south, east, and west.
east	East is one of the four main directions. East is the opposite of west.
Earth	Earth is the planet on which people live.
far	Far is a word that tells where things are. Far is the opposite of near.
globe	A globe is a model of Earth.
hill	A hill is land that is higher than a plain but not as high as a mountain.
lake	A lake is a body of water that has land all around it.
left	Left is a word that tells where things are. Left is the opposite of right.
map	A map is a drawing of a place from above. A map shows part or all of Earth.

map key	A map key is a list of symbols used on a map. The map key tells what each symbol means.
mountain	A mountain is very high land.
near	Near is a word that tells where things are. Near is the opposite of far.
neighborhood	A neighborhood is a place where people live and work.
north	North is one of the four main directions. North is the direction toward the North Pole.
ocean	An ocean is a very large body of water. Earth has five oceans.
plain	A plain is flat land.
right	Right is a word that tells where things are. Right is the opposite of left.
river	A river is a body of water that flows across the land.
route	A route is a way to go from one place to another.
south	South is one of the four main directions. South is the direction toward the South Pole.
state	A state is part of the United States. There are 50 states.
symbol	A symbol is a drawing that stands for something real.
west	West is one of the four main directions. West is the opposite of east.

Scholastic Professional Books

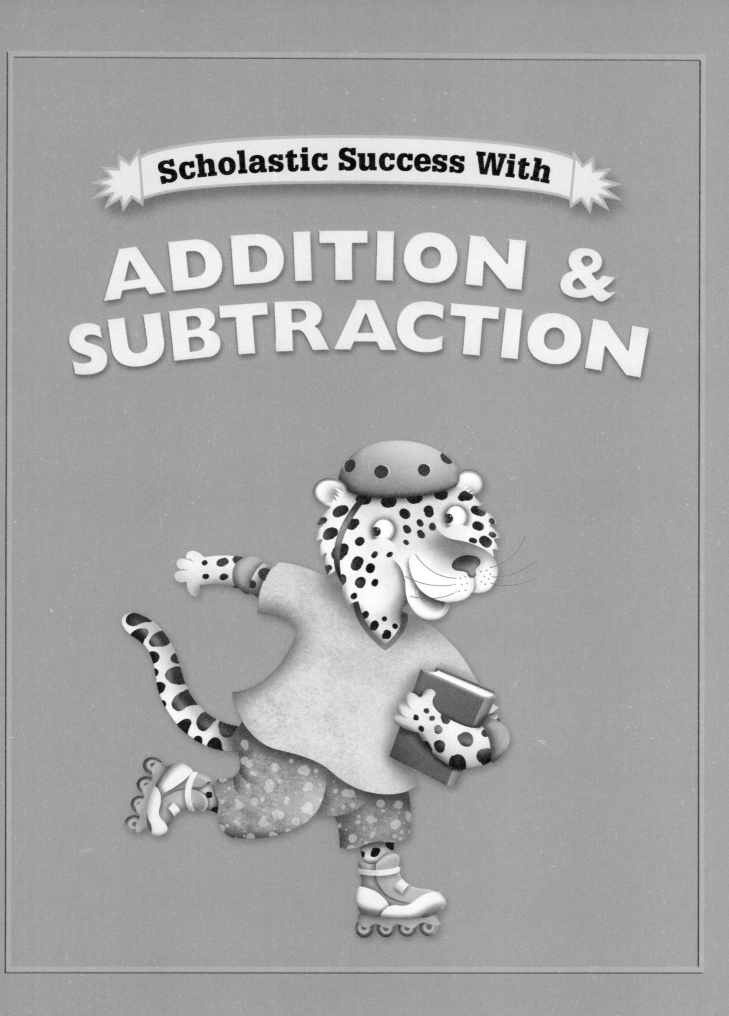

Scholastic Success With

ADDITION & SUBTRACTION

Clowning Around

Add. Color the picture using the color code.

5 + 2 =

6 + 3 =

$\begin{array}{r} 4 \\ + 5 \\ \hline \end{array}$

$\begin{array}{r} 5 \\ + 0 \\ \hline \end{array}$

$\begin{array}{r} 2 \\ + 3 \\ \hline \end{array}$

$\begin{array}{r} 7 \\ + 2 \\ \hline \end{array}$

$\begin{array}{r} 4 \\ + 4 \\ \hline \end{array}$

2 + 5 =

3 + 2 =

$\begin{array}{r} 4 \\ + 3 \\ \hline \end{array}$

$\begin{array}{r} 3 \\ + 3 \\ \hline \end{array}$

$\begin{array}{r} 1 \\ + 0 \\ \hline \end{array}$

$\begin{array}{r} 4 \\ + 2 \\ \hline \end{array}$

$\begin{array}{r} 0 \\ + 1 \\ \hline \end{array}$

$\begin{array}{r} 5 \\ + 1 \\ \hline \end{array}$

4 + 1 =

$\begin{array}{r} 6 \\ + 2 \\ \hline \end{array}$

$\begin{array}{r} 2 \\ + 1 \\ \hline \end{array}$

$\begin{array}{r} 3 \\ + 0 \\ \hline \end{array}$

$\begin{array}{r} 3 \\ + 5 \\ \hline \end{array}$

7 + 0 =

5 + 5 =

6 + 1 =

$\begin{array}{r} 1 \\ + 1 \\ \hline \end{array}$

7 + 3 =

3 + 1 =

Lovely Ladybugs

Write a number sentence to show how many spots each ladybug has.

$1 + 2 = 3$

___ + ___ = ___

___ + ___ = ___

___ + ___ = ___

___ + ___ = ___

___ + ___ = ___

___ + ___ = ___

___ + ___ = ___

___ + ___ = ___

Color the ladybug with the greatest number of spots red.

Color the ladybug with the least number of spots blue.

Beautiful Bouquets

Look at the number on each bow. Draw more flowers to match the number written on the bow.

Color the bows with an even number yellow.
Color the bows with an odd number purple.

Telephone Math

What kind of phone never rings? _____

To find out, solve the addition problems. Then use the code on the telephone to replace your answers with letters. The first one has been done for you.

6		
+ 2	A	
8		

5		4		3	
+ 1	___	+ 4	___	+ 6	___

3		3		2	
+ 0	___	+ 4	___	+ 2	___

2		1		0	
+ 1	___	+ 1	___	+ 1	___

Write your telephone number in letters using the phone code above.

_____

High Flyer

Do the subtraction problems.

> If the answer is 1 or 2, color the shape red.
>
> If the answer is 3 or 4, color the shape blue.
>
> If the answer is 5 or 6, color the shape yellow.
>
> If the answer is 7 or 8, color the shape green.
>
> If the answer is 9, color the shape black.
>
> Color the other shapes the colors of your choice.

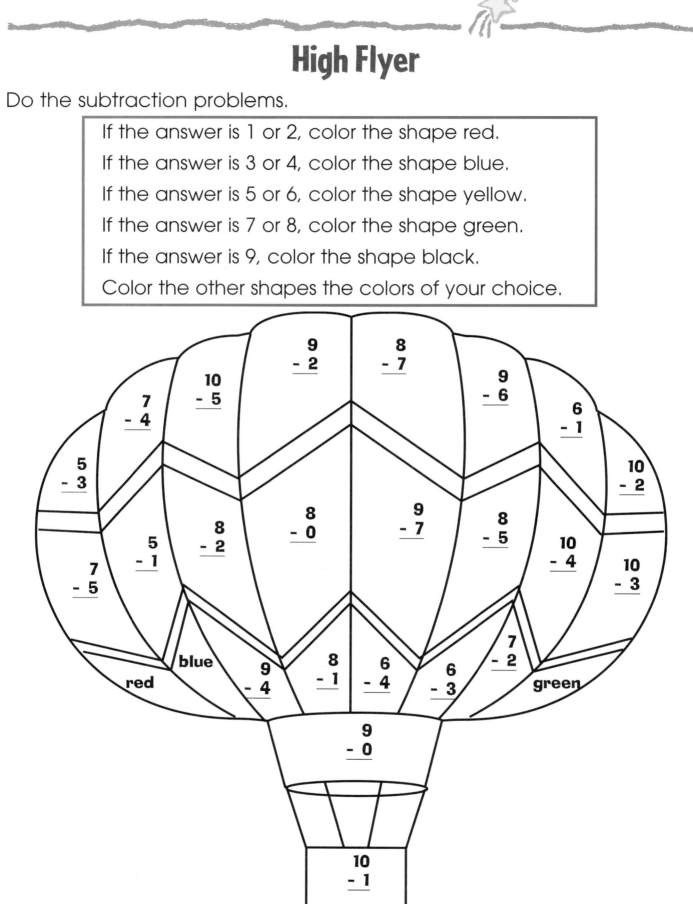

Scholastic Professional Books

Juggling Act

Cross out. Write how many are left.

$4 - 2 =$ ____

$3 - 1 =$ __2__

$7 - 4 =$ ____

$9 - 6 =$ ____

$5 - 3 =$ ____

$6 - 5 =$ ____

Ocean Life

Use the math picture on page 309 to count and write the number in each box. Subtract the numbers.

Coloring Key

dark blue

pink

dark gray

light gray

light blue

dark brown

white

brown

peach

black

Trucking Along

Subtract. Color the picture using the color code.

Color Code

0	white
1	brown
2	black
3	green
4	purple
5	orange
6	yellow
7	blue
8	red

$7 - 6 =$

$9 - 1 =$

$\begin{array}{r} 9 \\ -\ 2 \\ \hline \end{array}$

$\begin{array}{r} 8-4= \end{array}$ $7-3=$ $6-2=$

$4 - 4 =$

$\begin{array}{r} 10 \\ -\ 6 \\ \hline \end{array}$

$\begin{array}{r} 9 \\ -\ 5 \\ \hline \end{array}$

$\begin{array}{r} 1 \\ -\ 1 \\ \hline \end{array}$

$\begin{array}{r} 5 \\ -\ 2 \\ \hline \end{array}$

$10 - 2 =$

$\begin{array}{r} 10 \\ -\ 7 \\ \hline \end{array}$

$10 - 4 =$

$\begin{array}{r} 8 \\ -\ 2 \\ \hline \end{array}$

$\begin{array}{r} 10 \\ -\ 9 \\ \hline \end{array}$

$6 - 3 =$

$9 - 4 =$

$9 - 7 =$

$\begin{array}{r} 9 \\ -\ 3 \\ \hline \end{array}$

$10 - 8 =$

$7 - 5 =$

$\begin{array}{r} 9 \\ -\ 6 \\ \hline \end{array}$

$8 - 2 =$

$\begin{array}{r} 4 \\ -\ 3 \\ \hline \end{array}$

$\begin{array}{r} 9 \\ -\ 1 \\ \hline \end{array}$

Scholastic Professional Books

Night Lights

Subtract. Connect the dots from greatest to least.

$10 - 3 =$ ☐ •

$9 - 1 =$ ☐

$8 - 2 =$ ☐

$10 - 1 =$ ☐ •

• $9 - 4 =$ ☐

$10 - 0 =$ ☐ •

• $7 - 3 =$ ☐

$5 - 3 =$ ☐

$6 - 5 =$ ☐ •

• $8 - 5 =$ ☐

Subtract. Connect the dots from least to greatest.

$10 - 0 =$ ☐ • - - • $9 - 8 =$ ☐

• $7 - 5 =$ ☐

$10 - 1 =$ ☐ •

• $10 - 7 =$ ☐

$10 - 2 =$ ☐ •

$7 - 0 =$ ☐ •

• $6 - 2 =$ ☐

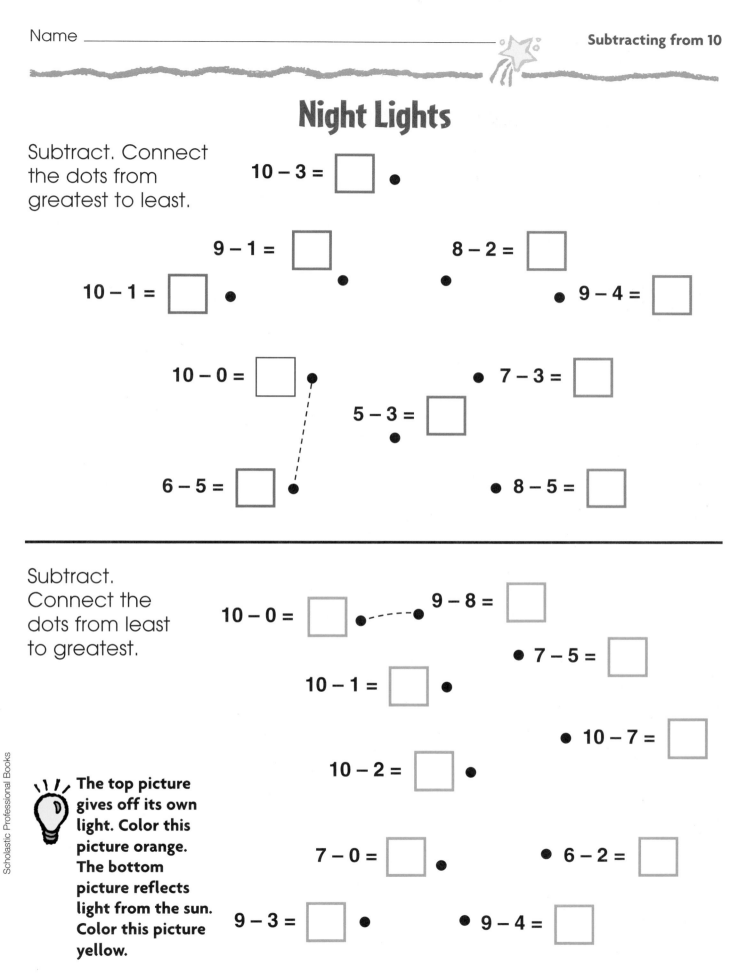

The top picture gives off its own light. Color this picture orange. The bottom picture reflects light from the sun. Color this picture yellow.

$9 - 3 =$ ☐ •

• $9 - 4 =$ ☐

Hop to It: Add and Subtract

Add or subtract. Trace the number line with your finger to check your work.

Examples: **4 + 5 = _____**   **4 − 2 = _____**

Start on **4**.   Start on **4**.

Move **5** 🥕 right.   Move **2** 🥕 left.

7 − 3 = _____	**9 − 6 = _____**	**2 + 0 = _____**
5 + 5 = _____	**8 − 7 = _____**	**4 + 3 = _____**
10 − 4 = _____	**6 + 2 = _____**	**7 − 2 = _____**

Circle the answer to each question.

What direction did 🐰 **move to add?**   left or right

What direction did 🐰 **move to subtract?**   left or right

Mitten Matchup

Add or subtract. Draw a line to match mittens with the same answer.

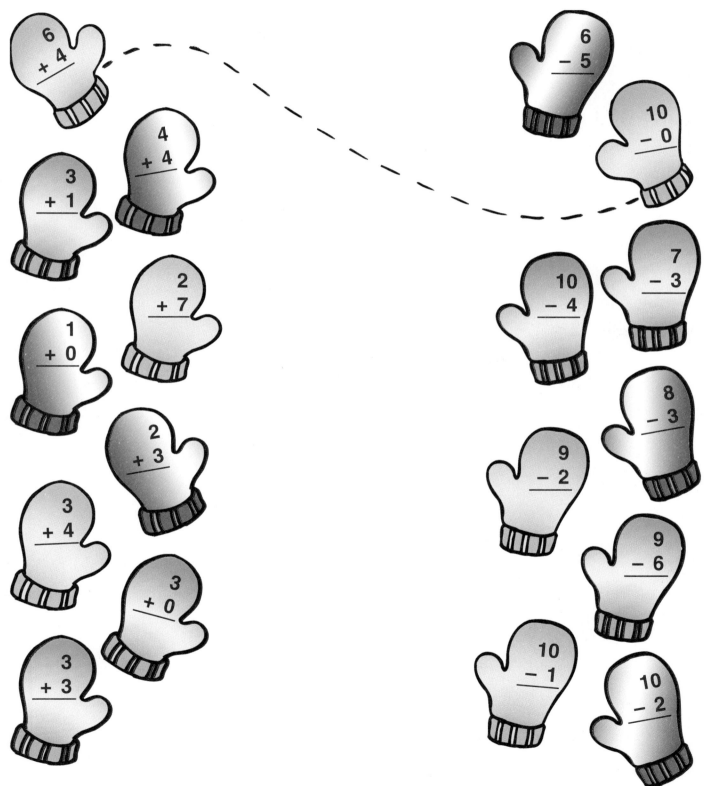

$$6 + 4$$

$$4 + 4$$

$$3 + 1$$

$$2 + 7$$

$$1 + 0$$

$$2 + 3$$

$$3 + 4$$

$$3 + 0$$

$$3 + 3$$

$$6 - 5$$

$$10 - 0$$

$$10 - 4$$

$$7 - 3$$

$$8 - 3$$

$$9 - 2$$

$$9 - 6$$

$$10 - 1$$

$$10 - 2$$

Blast Off

Add or subtract. Then use the code to answer the riddle below.

$3 + 4$ S

$9 - 5 = 4$ H

$8 - 8$ D

$6 + 4$ F

$7 - 6$ O

$6 - 4$ L

$2 + 3$ U

$2 + 7$ T

$8 - 2$ W

$4 + 4$ I

$10 - 7$ R

How is an astronaut's job unlike any other job?

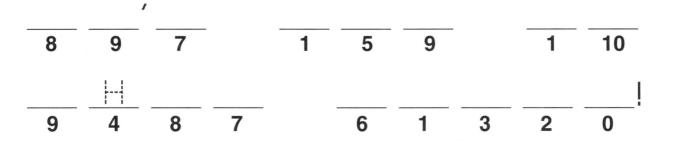

__ __ __ , __ __ __ __ __
8 9 7   1 5 9   1 10

__ H __ __   __ __ __ __ __!
9 4 8 7   6 1 3 2 0

Scholastic Professional Books

Out on the Town

Color a box on the graph for each item in the picture.

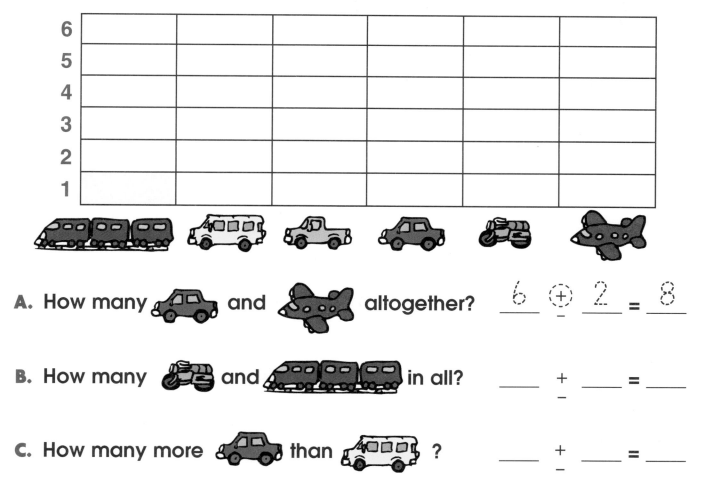

A. How many 🚗 and ✈ altogether? 6 (+) 2 = 8

B. How many 🏍 and 🚃 in all? ____ + ____ = ____
                                          −

C. How many more 🚗 than 🚌 ? ____ + ____ = ____
                                          −

Shapes on a Snake

Add or subtract.

A. ♥6 + ⬭4 = 10

B. ⬜ − ◇ = _____

C. ○ − ⬡ = _____

D. ⬭ + ♥ = _____

E. ▭ + ⬡ = _____

F. ⬡ + ⬡ = _____

G. ◇ + ⬡ = _____

H. ♥ + ⬭ = _____

I. △ − ▭ = _____

J. ⬜ − ⬡ = _____

Planes . . . Trains . . .

Add or subtract.

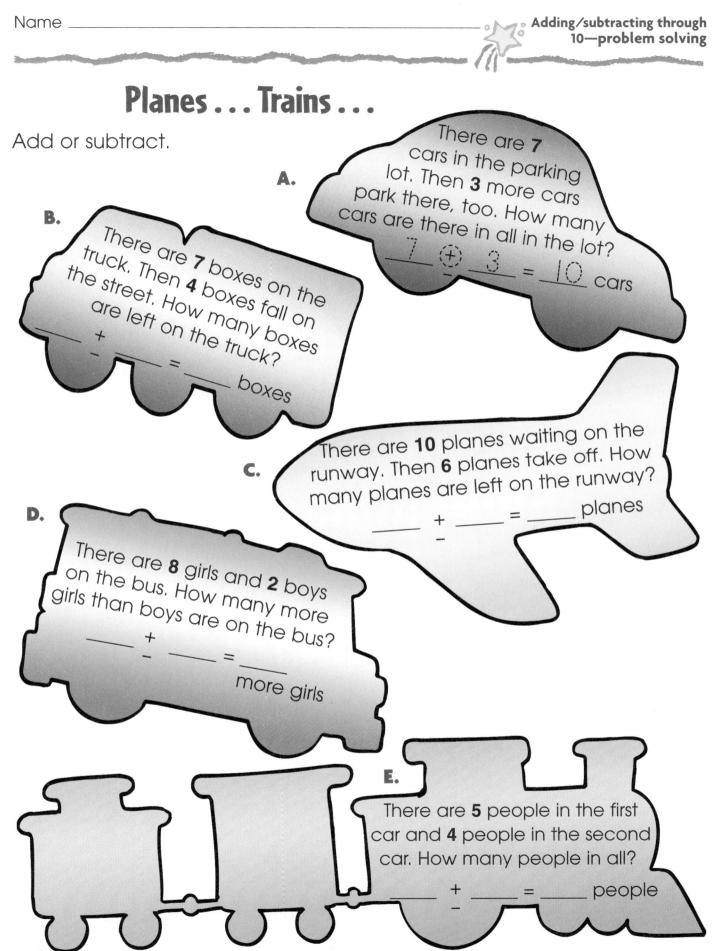

A. There are **7** cars in the parking lot. Then **3** more cars park there, too. How many cars are there in all in the lot?

7 ⊕ 3 = 10 cars

B. There are **7** boxes on the truck. Then **4** boxes fall on the street. How many boxes are left on the truck?

___ + ___ = ___ boxes
   −

C. There are **10** planes waiting on the runway. Then **6** planes take off. How many planes are left on the runway?

___ + ___ = ___ planes
   −

D. There are **8** girls and **2** boys on the bus. How many more girls than boys are on the bus?

___ + ___ = ___
   −
more girls

E. There are **5** people in the first car and **4** people in the second car. How many people in all?

___ + ___ = ___ people
   −

Slice It Up

Add. Color the picture using the color code.

14 + 4 =
13 + 2 =
18 + 0 =
6 + 10 =
8 + 9 =
16 + 2 =
11 + 3 =
9 + 7 =
10 + 8 =
10 + 8 =
12 + 4 =
12 + 5 =
11 + 6 =
7 + 7 =
8 + 7 =
11 + 4 =
9 + 5 =
7 + 11 =
13 + 4 =
12 + 2 =
13 + 3 =
6 + 9 =
14 + 1 =
12 + 3 =
12 + 6 =
9 + 9 =
14 + 2 =
12 + 6 =
14 + 3 =
13 + 5 =
10 + 4 =
8 + 8 =
7 + 10 =
11 + 7 =
8 + 6 =
17 + 1 =

Color Code	brown	green	red	yellow	tan
	14	15	16	17	18

How many different ways can you make a sum of 10? Show your work on another piece of paper.

Leap on Over

Add. To show the frog's path across the pond, color each lily pad green if the sum is greater than 10.

10 + 1 =

6 + 4 =

6 + 9 =

5 + 2 =

7 + 0 =

5 + 5 =

9 + 2 =

10 + 4 =

3 + 7 =

7 + 6 =

4 + 3 =

5 + 4 =

3 + 8 =

2 + 2 =

8 + 8 =

How many leaps did the frog take across the pond? _____

Animal Mystery

What kind of animal always carries a trunk?

_____

To find out, solve the addition problems. If the answer is greater than 9, color the shape yellow. If the answer is less than 10, color the shape gray.

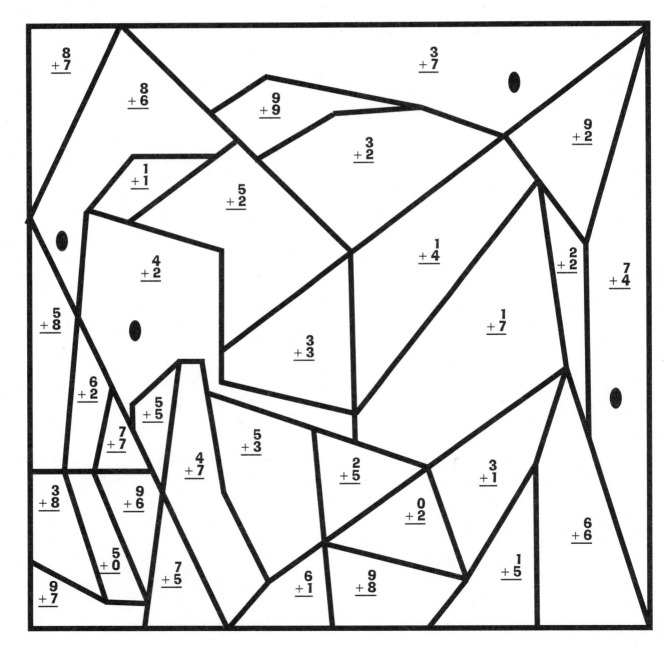

Scholastic Professional Books

Scarecrow Sam

Why doesn't Scarecrow Sam tell secrets when he is near Farmer Joe's bean patch? _____

To find out the answer, add the numbers. Circle the pumpkins that have sums of 14, and write the letters that appear inside those pumpkins in the boxes below.

1. 4 + 2 G
2. 7 + 7 B
3. 9 + 5 E
4. 10 + 4 A
5. 4 + 8 R
6. 6 + 8 N
7. 11 + 3 S
8. 14 + 0 T
9. 7 + 2 P
10. 13 + 1 A
11. 5 + 8 S
12. 12 + 2 L
13. 7 + 4 H
14. 5 + 9 K

Scholastic Professional Books

Flying High

Add down and across to find the missing number.

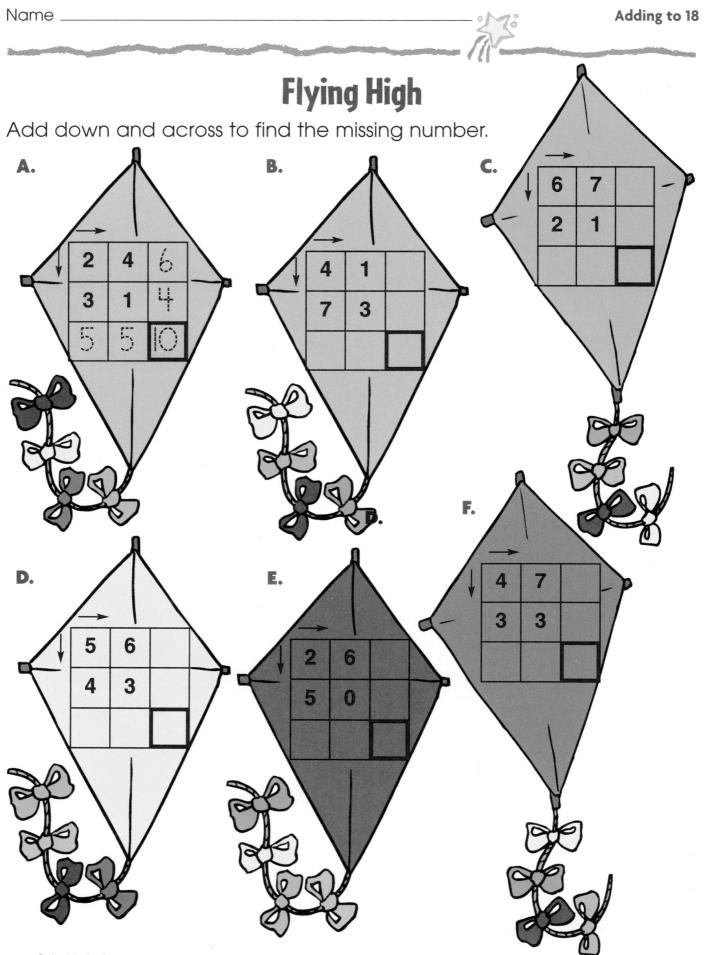

A.

2	4	6
3	1	4
5	5	10

B.

4	1	
7	3	

C.

6	7	
2	1	

D.

5	6	
4	3	

E.

2	6	
5	0	

F.

4	7	
3	3	

Double Dips

Write the doubles that equal the number on the cone.

Circle the answer.

When adding doubles, the sum will always be: even   odd

Not Far From Home

Start at 🏠. Write the number of steps. Add.

| steps to + steps home = _____ steps | steps to + steps home = _____ steps |

$$7 + 7 = 14$$

Break the Code

Subtract.

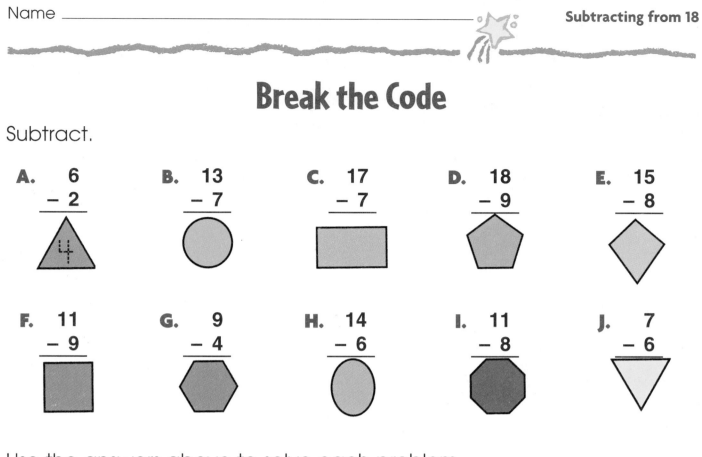

A.   6
   − 2
= 4

B.   13
   − 7

C.   17
   − 7

D.   18
   − 9

E.   15
   − 8

F.   11
   − 9

G.   9
   − 4

H.   14
   − 6

I.   11
   − 8

J.   7
   − 6

Use the answers above to solve each problem.

K.   L.   M.   N.

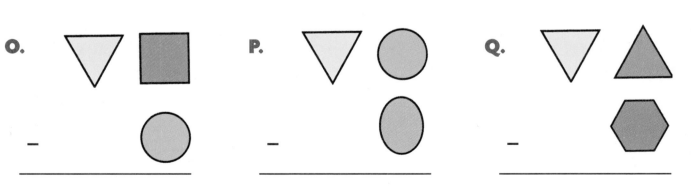

O.   P.   Q.

The Big Search

Subtract. Circle the difference.

11 – 7 = five three (four)	**14 – 9 =** nine one five
13 – 6 = six nine seven	**16 – 5 =** twelve thirteen eleven
18 – 9 = eleven ten nine	**17 – 11 =** seven six ten
15 – 5 = ten seven five	**12 – 9 =** three two four
12 – 4 = six eight nine	**11 – 9 =** three five two

Find each circled number in the word puzzle. Look → and ↓.

```
f o u r h i o n e g s k m
i f o n t g y f a f u e z
f t l u e j s i x s b x t
t t w e l v e v k s t l h
e p n i n e w e j e r t i
e d n g q i h r y v a q r
n v h h o t h r e e c s t
d m k t c w b t e n t r e
x d i p g o a c p f i s e
c e l e v e n a b z o v n
b w u d i f f e r e n c e
```

See if you can find these number words: twelve, fifteen, thirteen, subtraction, difference.

Scholastic Professional Books

Race Through the Facts

Add or subtract. The race car that ends with the highest number wins the race!

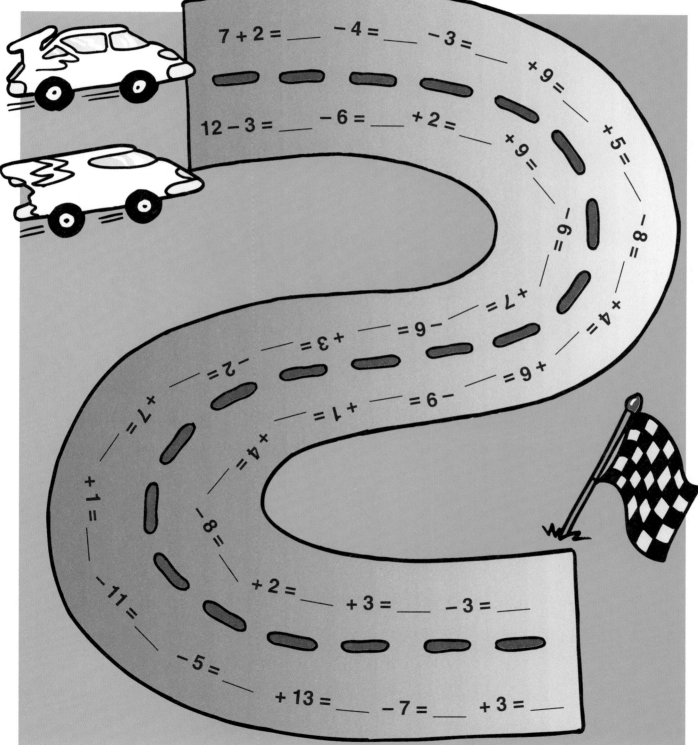

7 + 2 = ___ − 4 = ___ − 3 = ___ + 9 = ___ + 5 = ___ − 8 = ___

12 − 3 = ___ − 6 = ___ + 2 = ___ + 9 = ___ − 9 = ___ + 4 = ___ + 6 = ___ − 9 = ___ + 1 = ___ + 4 = ___ − 2 = ___ + 3 = ___ − 6 = ___ + 7 = ___

+ 7 = ___ + 1 = ___ − 8 = ___ + 2 = ___ + 3 = ___ − 3 = ___

− 11 = ___ − 5 = ___ + 13 = ___ − 7 = ___ + 3 = ___

💡 **Color the winning race car blue.**

Little Snacks

Add or subtract. Then follow the maze through the even answers.

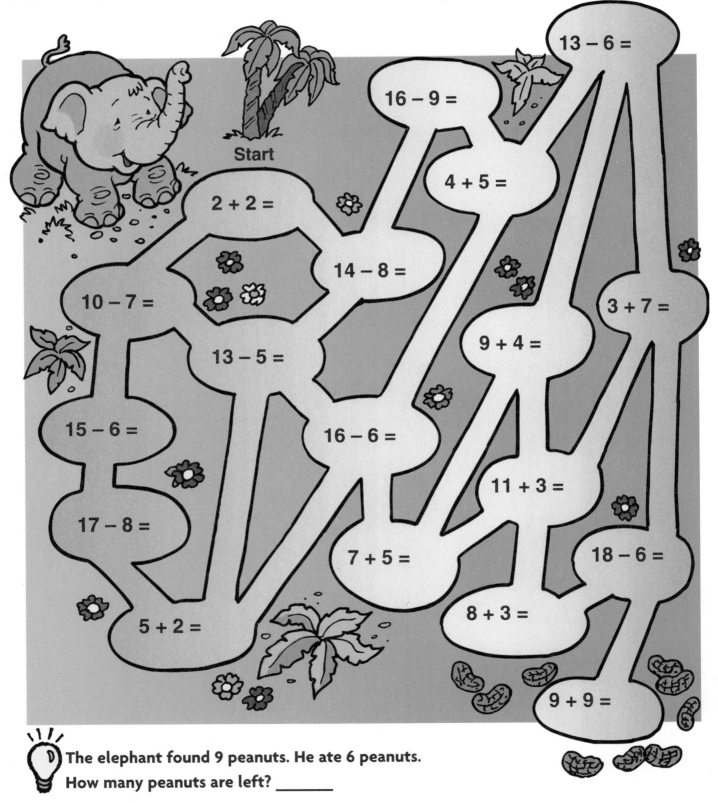

Start

13 − 6 =

16 − 9 =

4 + 5 =

2 + 2 =

14 − 8 =

10 − 7 =

3 + 7 =

13 − 5 =

9 + 4 =

15 − 6 =

16 − 6 =

11 + 3 =

17 − 8 =

7 + 5 =

18 − 6 =

5 + 2 =

8 + 3 =

9 + 9 =

**The elephant found 9 peanuts. He ate 6 peanuts.
How many peanuts are left? _____**

Name _____

Flying Families

Fill in the missing number for each family. Use the numbers from the box.

| 9 | 12 | 15 | 8 | 10 |
| 6 | 4 | 7 | 5 | 11 | 2 |

Fill in the families with twins.

Colorful Flowers

Color a box on the graph for each item in the picture.

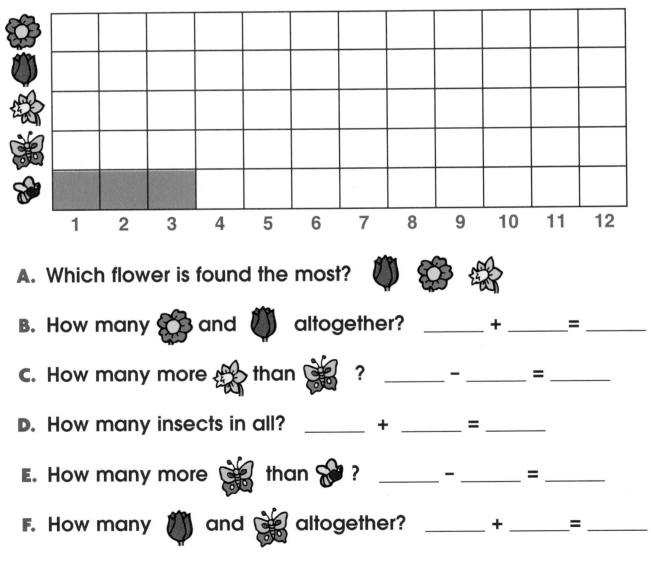

A. Which flower is found the most?

B. How many 🌼 and 🌷 altogether? _____ + _____ = _____

C. How many more 🌻 than 🦋 ? _____ – _____ = _____

D. How many insects in all? _____ + _____ = _____

E. How many more 🦋 than 🐝 ? _____ – _____ = _____

F. How many 🌷 and 🦋 altogether? _____ + _____ = _____

A Nutty Bunch

Add or subtract. Color the nut brown if the answer matches the squirrel.

A.

15 − 3 =

17 − 4 =

6 + 7 =

11 + 2 =

13

B.

8 + 3 =

15 − 4 =

9 + 3 =

18 − 7 =

11

C.

9 + 6 =

18 − 3 =

13 + 4 =

15 + 2 =

17

D.

12 + 2 =

9 + 5 =

17 − 3 =

11 + 5 =

14

💡 **Create a nutty bunch.**

16

Penguin Parade

Add or subtract. Write the pattern on the flag.

$5 + 7$

$8 + 3$

$15 - 5$

$18 - 9$

$11 - 3$

$12 - 5$

$9 - 7$

$12 - 8$

$5 + 1$

$16 - 8$

$13 - 3$

$7 + 5$

$12 - 9$

$11 - 5$

$13 - 4$

$7 + 5$

$18 - 3$

$11 + 7$

$15 - 2$

$4 + 7$

$12 - 3$

$12 - 5$

$8 - 3$

$12 - 9$

Scholastic Professional Books

A Perfect Strike

Fill in the missing number.

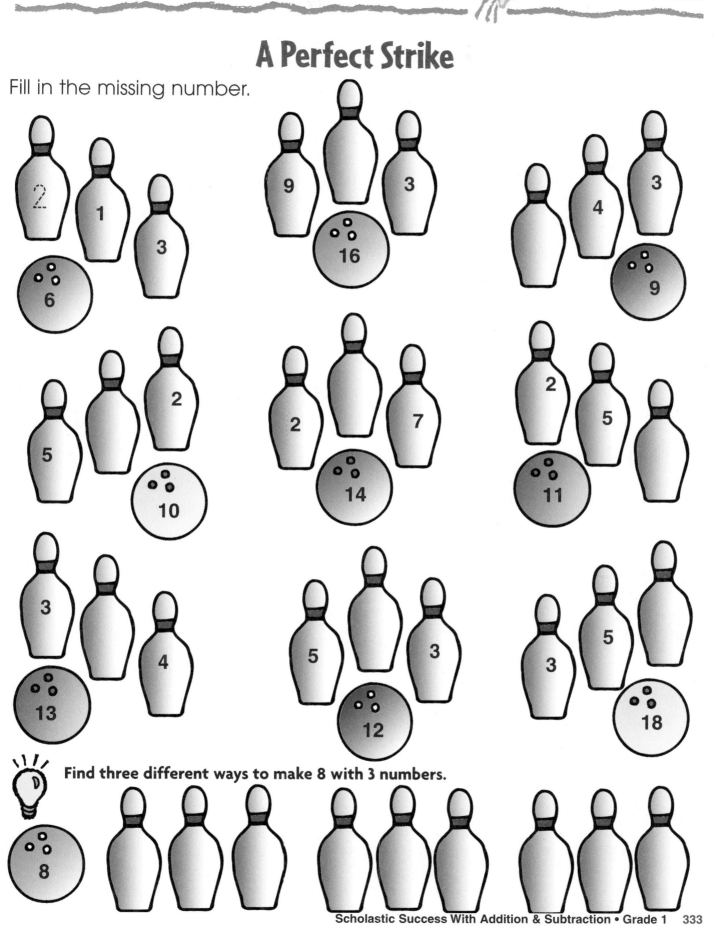

Find three different ways to make 8 with 3 numbers.

What a Treat!

Find the number in the mouse and cheese. ☐

Find the sum of the numbers in the cheese.

_____ + _____ + _____ = _____

Find the sum of the numbers in the mouse.

_____ + _____ + _____ = _____

Find the number in the
rabbit and carrot. ☐

Find the sum of the largest number in the
rabbit and the smallest number in the carrot.

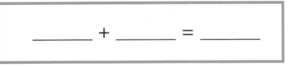

_____ + _____ = _____

Find the difference between the largest
and smallest number in the carrot.

_____ − _____ = _____

 Find the sum of all the numbers in the mouse and cheese.

_____ + _____ + _____ + _____ + _____ = _____

Find the sum of all the numbers in the rabbit and carrot.

_____ + _____ + _____ + _____ + _____ = _____

Scholastic Professional Books

Have a Heart

Circle a group of 10. Write the number of tens and ones.

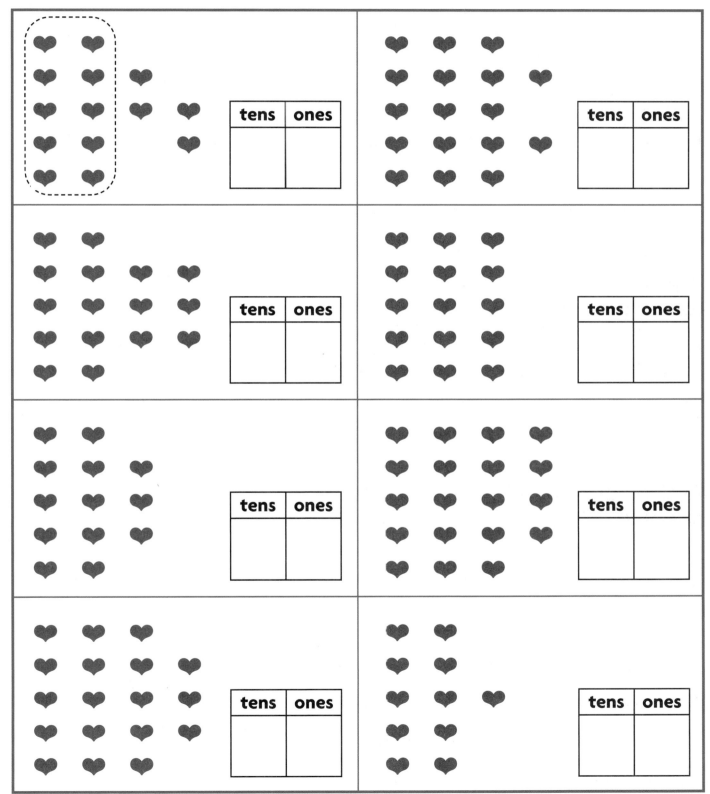

Beautiful Butterflies

Add. Color the picture using the color code.

Color Code

26	red
29	orange
38	green
54	purple
87	yellow

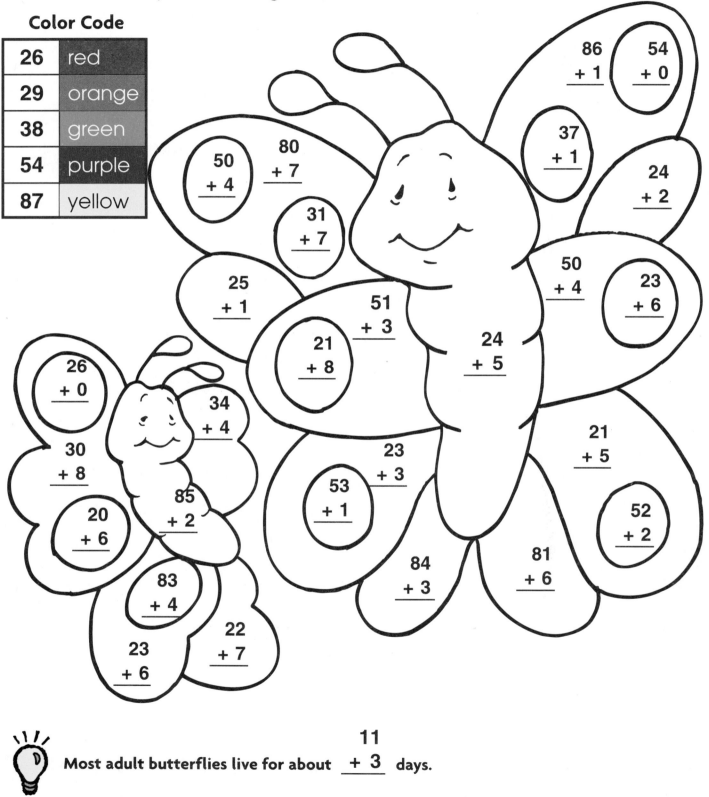

Most adult butterflies live for about $\begin{array}{r} 11 \\ +\ 3 \\ \hline \end{array}$ days.

Scholastic Professional Books

Where's the Beach?

Add. To find the path to the beach, color each box with an odd answer yellow.

14 + 3	34 + 2	81 + 3

76 + 2	25 + 4	56 + 3	11 + 3	40 + 8
87 + 1	22 + 2	32 + 3	65 + 1	93 + 5
10 + 8	41 + 2	70 + 7	32 + 6	84 + 4
73 + 5	63 + 2	55 + 1	41 + 5	23 + 3

98 + 1	53 + 4	82 + 5

By the Seashore

Use the code below to write each missing number. Add.

93
+ _____
_____

82
+ _____
_____

14
+ _____
_____

21
+ _____
_____

53
+ _____
_____

45
+ _____
_____

73
+ _____
_____

36
+ _____
_____

61
+ _____
_____

32
+ _____
_____

4

7

5

3

6

Find the sum for all the shells. _____ + _____ + _____ + _____ + _____ = _____

Sail Away

Finish each addition sentence. Add.

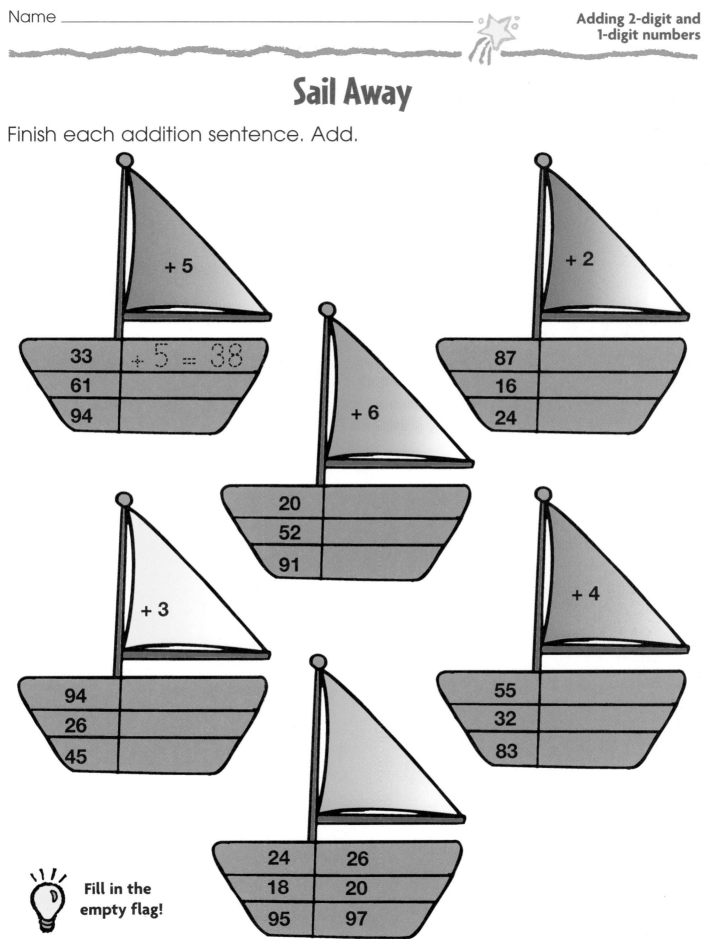

	+5
33	+ 5 = 38
61	
94	

	+2
87	
16	
24	

	+6
20	
52	
91	

	+3
94	
26	
45	

	+4
55	
32	
83	

24	26
18	20
95	97

Fill in the
empty flag!

Dino-Math

Subtract. Color the picture using the color code.

Color Code

16	red
22	orange
34	purple
57	blue
73	yellow
85	green

$$87 - 2$$

$$89 - 4$$

$$27 - 5$$

$$19 - 3$$

$$88 - 3$$

$$39 - 5$$

$$34 - 0$$

$$86 - 1$$

$$78 - 5$$

$$85 - 0$$

$$58 - 1$$

$$28 - 6$$

$$77 - 4$$

$$38 - 4$$

$$29 - 7$$

$$35 - 1$$

Number Buddies

Subtract. Remember: the largest number always goes on top!

A. 7   39

3	9
■	7

_____

B. 54   1

■	

_____

C. 87   6

■	

_____

D. 73   3

■	

_____

E. 25   4

■	

_____

F. 42   2

■	

_____

G. 7   98

■	

_____

H. 5   66

■	

_____

Fill in each missing number.

39   35

27   20

88   83

Treasure Island

Subtract.

43 − 1	95 − 5	79 − 3	36 − 4	89 − 7	66 − 3	83 − 2
59 − 9	37 − 2	24 − 3	27 − 6	42 − 1	90 − 0	55 − 2
33 − 3	84 − 4	28 − 8	71 − 1	62 − 2	68 − 3	77 − 3

Use the clues to find the gold, the ship, and the treasure in the boxes above.

Find the gold. The difference is greater than **50** and less than **55**. Color the box with the gold yellow.

Find the ship. The difference is greater than **30** and less than **35**. Color the box with the ship orange.

Find the sunken treasure. The difference is greater than **70** and less than **75**. Color the box with the treasure red.

Name _____

Riding on Air

Add. Color the picture using the color code.

$42 + 53$

$31 + 23$

$46 + 32$

$24 + 13 =$

$23 + 55$

$24 + 62$

$64 + 14$

$60 + 18$

$65 + 21$

$75 + 11$

$53 + 33$

$24 + 30$

$15 + 22 =$

$42 + 12$

$11 + 13 =$

$54 + 32$

$42 + 36$

$15 + 22$

$72 + 23 =$

$25 + 24 =$

$36 + 13 =$

$37 + 12 =$

Color Code

24	red
37	blue
49	brown
54	white
78	yellow
86	purple
95	green

Number Puzzler

Can you spell 80 in two letters?

To find out how, do the addition problems. If the answer is even, shade the square. If your answers are correct, the shaded squares will spell the answer.

12 + 13	24 + 34	22 + 21	77 + 22	35 + 43	52 + 12	40 + 52
11 + 31	30 + 39	46 + 52	15 + 12	10 + 71	63 + 11	13 + 80
36 + 32	30 + 10	11 + 11	15 + 4	20 + 21	15 + 11	22 + 33
14 + 14	13 + 16	10 + 20	14 + 25	11 + 20	15 + 21	20 + 31
36 + 52	21 + 32	10 + 50	44 + 41	24 + 43	31 + 21	13 + 82

Scholastic Professional Books

Color the Sunflower

Do the addition problems in the sunflower picture below. Then use the Color Key to tell you what color to make each answer.

Extra: Write your age on four flashcards, and then add a 6, 7, 8, and 9 to each of the cards. Practice the answers with a friend.

Color Key
56 = green
68 = orange
89 = yellow
97 = blue

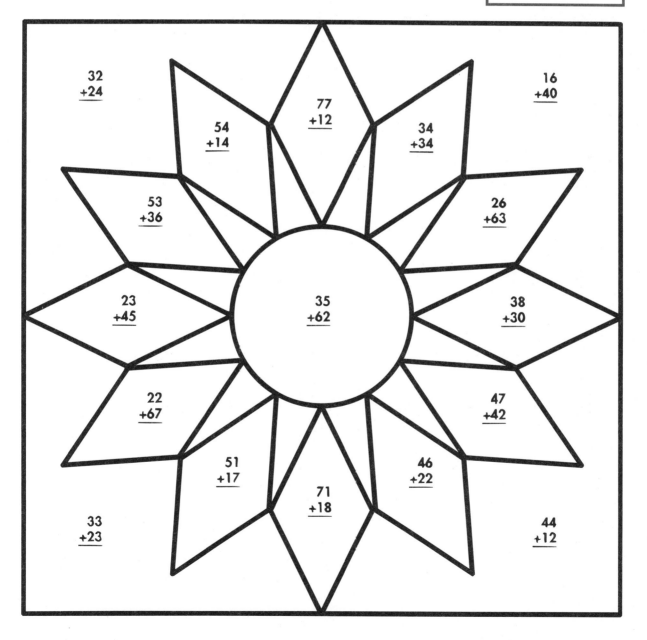

Roger the Rooster

Why did Roger the Rooster decide not to get in a barnyard fight?

To find out, add the numbers and shade the blocks as described below.

Shade the squares in row 1 that contain answers less than 25.

Shade the squares in row 2 that contain odd-numbered answers.

Shade the squares in row 3 that contain answers greater than 35.

Shade the squares in row 4 that contain even-numbered answers.

Shade the squares in row 5 that contain answers that end in zero.

13 + 11	26 + 33	16 + 31	10 + 12	64 + 24
H	**Y**	**O**	**E**	**U**
20 + 15	71 + 12	25 + 21	51 + 10	22 + 16
W	**A**	**W**	**S**	**O**
22 + 10	14 + 14	20 + 10	25 + 31	21 + 3
L	**C**	**E**	**A**	**L**
42 + 30	13 + 43	54 + 15	21 + 61	61 + 33
C	**H**	**F**	**I**	**C**
10 + 30	20 + 30	16 + 32	71 + 23	70 + 20
K	**E**	**J**	**S**	**N**

Scholastic Professional Books

Baseball Puzzle

What animal can always be found at a baseball game?

_____

To find out, do the subtraction problems. If the answer is greater
than 9, color the shapes black. If the answer is less than 10, color the
shapes red.

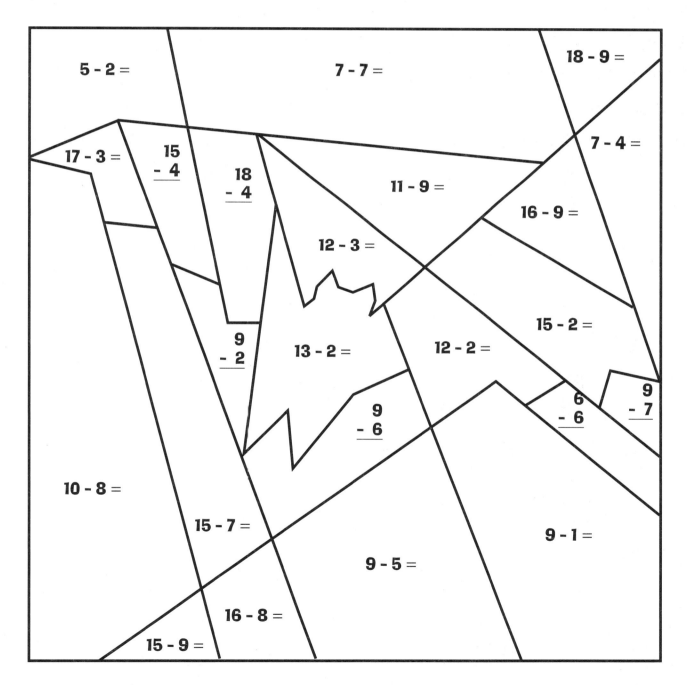

5 - 2 =

7 - 7 =

18 - 9 =

17 - 3 =

15
- 4

18
- 4

11 - 9 =

7 - 4 =

16 - 9 =

12 - 3 =

15 - 2 =

9
- 2

13 - 2 =

12 - 2 =

6
- 6

9
- 7

9
- 6

10 - 8 =

15 - 7 =

9 - 1 =

9 - 5 =

16 - 8 =

15 - 9 =

Color the Bowtie

Do the subtraction problems in the picture below. Then use the Color Key to tell you what color to make each answer.

Extra: On the back of this sheet of paper, draw a picture of four of your friends or family members. Give each one a bowtie!

Color Key

14 = red

26 = purple

33 = blue

47 = yellow

63 = green

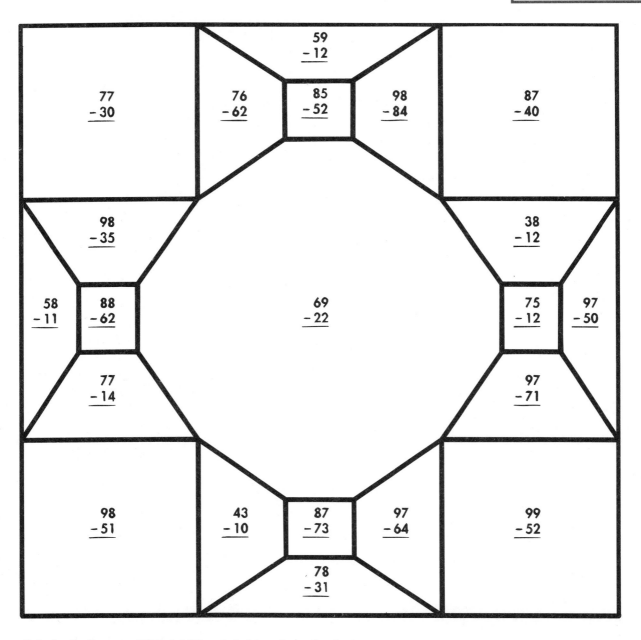

Scholastic Professional Books

Detective Work

Use the code to help Detective Dave discover the secret phone
number. The first problem has been done for you.

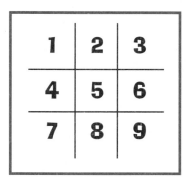

1	2	3
4	5	6
7	8	9

1.

$7 - 1 = 6$

2.

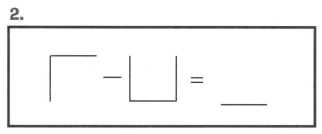

$\_ - \_ = \_$

3.

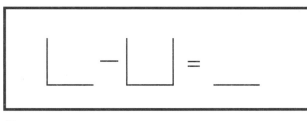

$\_ - \_ = \_$

4.

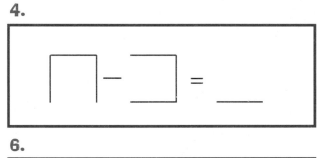

$\_ - \_ = \_$

5.

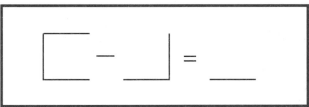

$\_ - \_ = \_$

6.

$\_ - \_ = \_$

7.

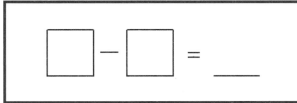

$\_ - \_ = \_$

The phone number is:

_ _ _ - _ _ _ _

Have a Ball

Subtract.

39
− 12

97
− 23

59
− 18

77
− 12

79
− 52

81
− 11

88
− 46

63
− 10

58
− 43

46
− 23

35
− 24

68
− 35

32
− 12

74
− 72

69
− 54

83
− 52

The Rams scored 49 points in the football game. The Bears scored 27 points. How many more points did the Rams score than the Bears? _____

Opposites Attract

Add or subtract. Connect the magnets that have the same answer.

42 + 33	new
32 + 54	laugh
35 + 12	open
13 + 10	sink
37 + 52	right

close	79 − 32
old	99 − 24
left	99 − 10
cry	98 − 12
float	48 − 25

On another piece of paper, write an addition and subtraction problem which have the same answer.

How Much Money?

Add to find out how much.

🖍️	3 4 ¢
🍬	+ 1 3 ¢
	———
	¢

🚗	¢
🏐	+ ¢
	———
	¢

🍎	¢
📘	+ ¢
	———
	¢

Subtract to find out how much.

🥫	¢
🖍️	− ¢
	———
	¢

📏	¢
🚗	− ¢
	———
	¢

🍎	¢
🍬	− ¢
	———
	¢

Snuggle Up With a Book

Day of the Week	Reading Minutes
Sunday	97
Monday	28
Tuesday	73
Wednesday	44
Thursday	51
Friday	45
Saturday	80

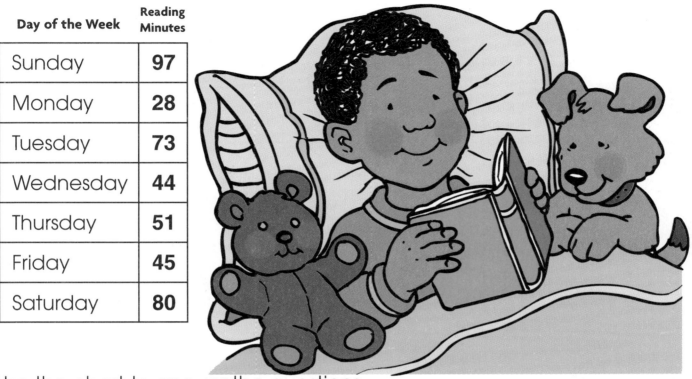

Use the chart to answer the questions.

A. What day did Alex read for the longest time?

_____

B. How many minutes did Alex read on Wednesday and Friday? _____ minutes

C. What day did Alex read for the shortest time?

_____

D. How many more minutes did Alex read on Sunday than Tuesday? _____ minutes

E. How many minutes did Alex read on Monday and Thursday? _____ minutes

F. How many more minutes did Alex read on Tuesday than Thursday? _____ minutes

One hour is 60 minutes. On what days did Alex read longer than one hour?

_____, _____, _____

Let the Sun Shine

Add or subtract. Then use the code to fill in the letters to finish each sun fact.

13	26	34	42	57	63	71	76	85	88
f	a	s	g	r	e	l	h	t	i

$$\begin{array}{r} 13 \\ +\ 21 \\ \hline \end{array} \qquad \begin{array}{r} 32 \\ +\ 53 \\ \hline \end{array} \qquad \begin{array}{r} 57 \\ -\ 31 \\ \hline \end{array} \qquad \begin{array}{r} 89 \\ -\ 32 \\ \hline \end{array}$$

The sun is a _____ _____ _____ _____.

$$\begin{array}{r} 30 \\ +\ 41 \\ \hline \end{array} \qquad \begin{array}{r} 98 \\ -\ 10 \\ \hline \end{array} \qquad \begin{array}{r} 12 \\ +\ 30 \\ \hline \end{array} \qquad \begin{array}{r} 97 \\ -\ 21 \\ \hline \end{array} \qquad \begin{array}{r} 99 \\ -\ 14 \\ \hline \end{array}$$

The sun gives _____ _____ _____ _____ _____ and

$$\begin{array}{r} 34 \\ +\ 42 \\ \hline \end{array} \qquad \begin{array}{r} 51 \\ +\ 12 \\ \hline \end{array} \qquad \begin{array}{r} 88 \\ -\ 62 \\ \hline \end{array} \qquad \begin{array}{r} 42 \\ +\ 43 \\ \hline \end{array}$$

_____ _____ _____ _____ to Earth.

$$\begin{array}{r} 88 \\ -\ 17 \\ \hline \end{array} \qquad \begin{array}{r} 56 \\ +\ 32 \\ \hline \end{array} \qquad \begin{array}{r} 49 \\ -\ 36 \\ \hline \end{array} \qquad \begin{array}{r} 30 \\ +\ 33 \\ \hline \end{array}$$

Without the sun, there would be no _____ _____ _____ _____.

Animal Surprises

Add or subtract. Match the answer to the animal fact.

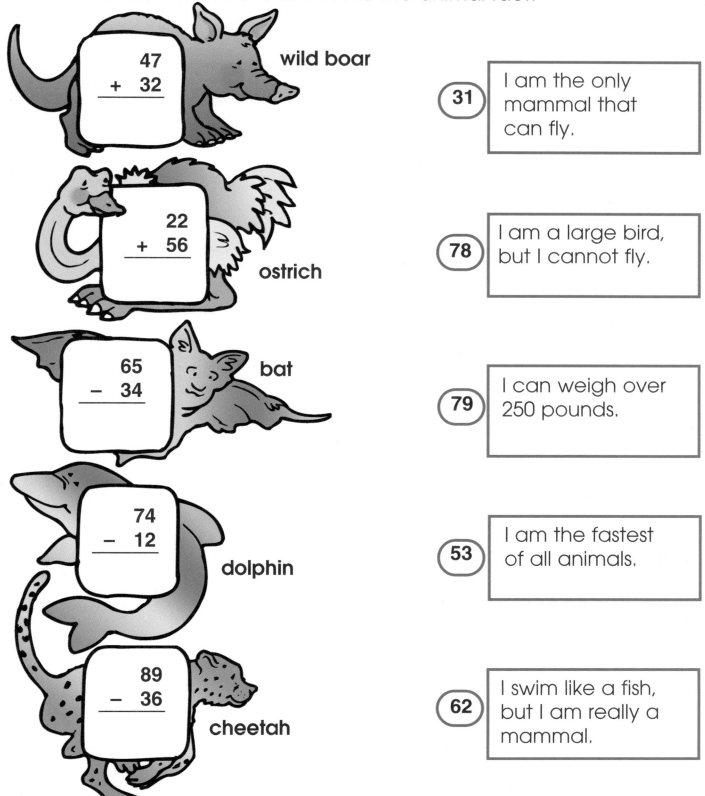

wild boar

$$\begin{array}{r} 47 \\ +\ 32 \\ \hline \end{array}$$

ostrich

$$\begin{array}{r} 22 \\ +\ 56 \\ \hline \end{array}$$

bat

$$\begin{array}{r} 65 \\ -\ 34 \\ \hline \end{array}$$

dolphin

$$\begin{array}{r} 74 \\ -\ 12 \\ \hline \end{array}$$

cheetah

$$\begin{array}{r} 89 \\ -\ 36 \\ \hline \end{array}$$

31 I am the only mammal that can fly.

78 I am a large bird, but I cannot fly.

79 I can weigh over 250 pounds.

53 I am the fastest of all animals.

62 I swim like a fish, but I am really a mammal.

Fishbowl

Add or subtract. Circle the fish that does not belong with the family.
Hint: Look at the tens place.

42 + 23

33 + 36

27 + 12

51 + 13

37 + 12

96 − 51

83 − 40

23 + 64

47 + 41

22 + 26

32 + 57

98 − 16

Make another family with 7 in the tens place.

Scholastic Professional Books

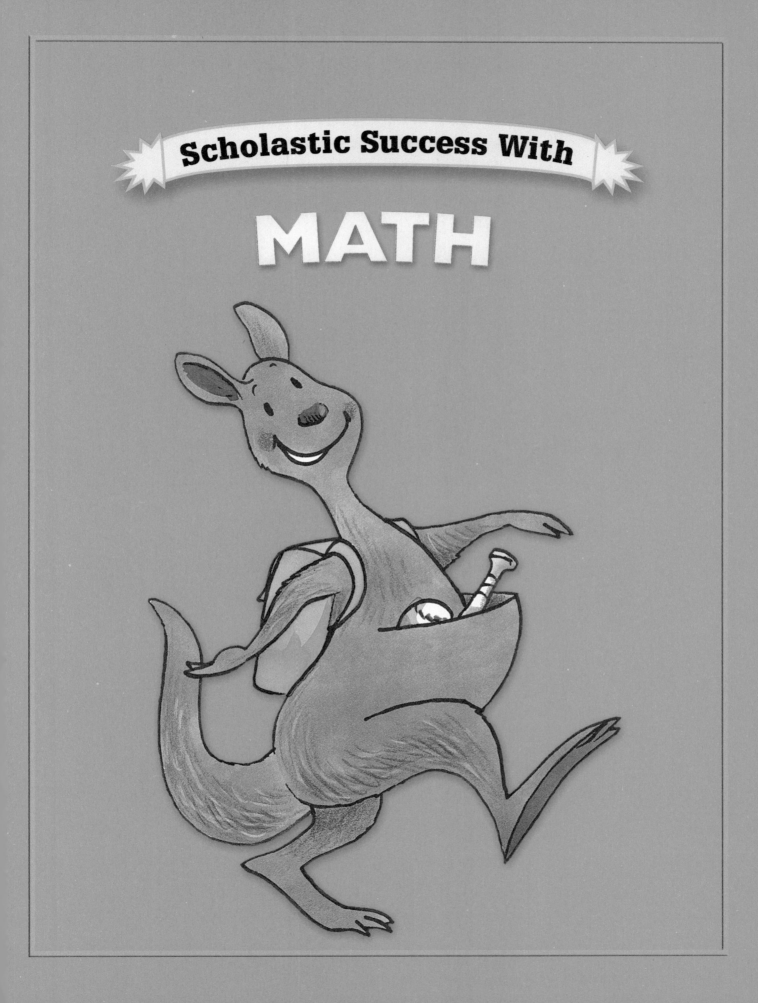

Scholastic Success With

MATH

Color the Basket

Count the number of dots or triangles in each shape. Then use the Color Key to tell you what color to make each shape. (For example, a shape with 7 dots will be colored green.)

Extra: On the back of this sheet of paper, draw a basket filled with six things you would carry in it.

Color Key
6 = yellow
7 = green
8 = brown
9 = red
10 = green

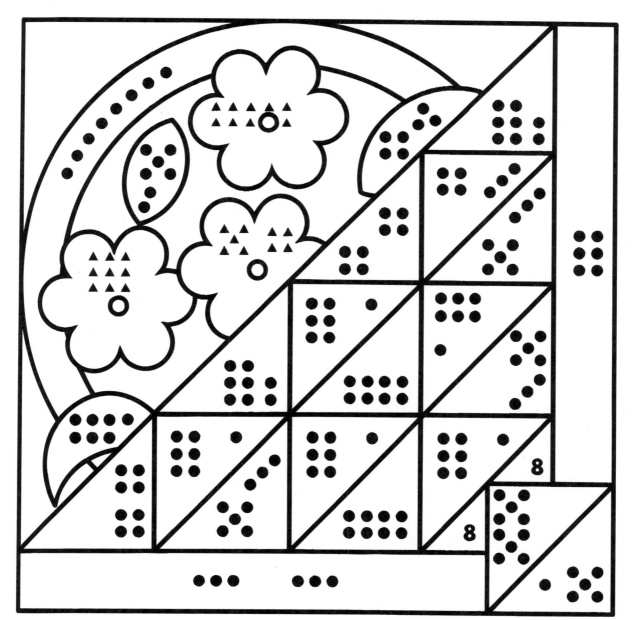

Number User

I use numbers to tell about myself.

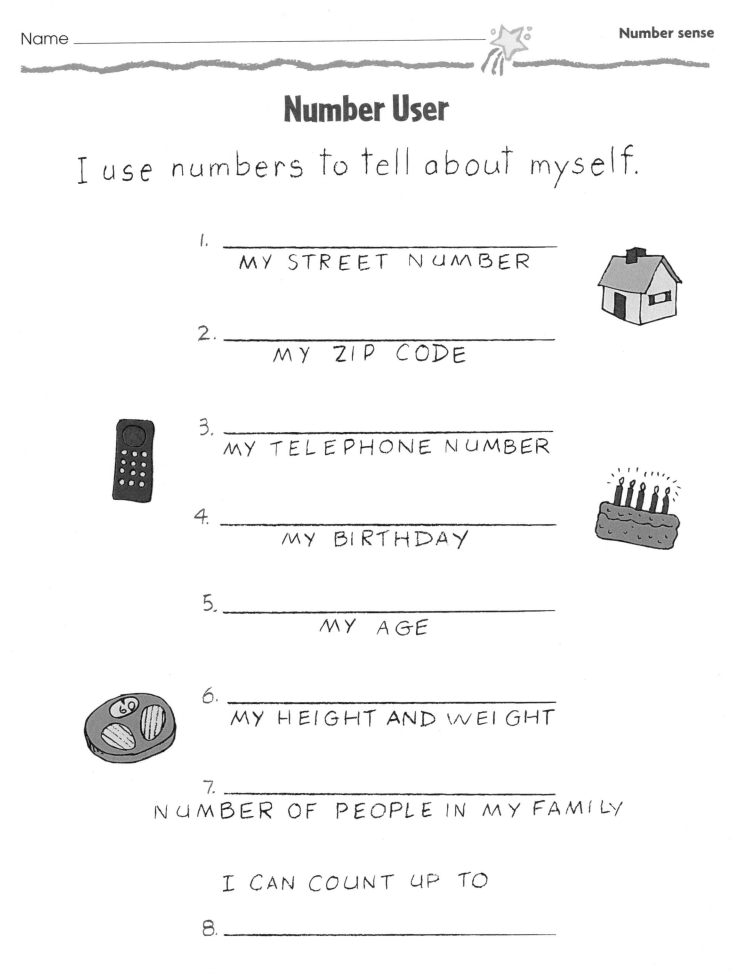

1. _____
MY STREET NUMBER

2. _____
MY ZIP CODE

3. _____
MY TELEPHONE NUMBER

4. _____
MY BIRTHDAY

5. _____
MY AGE

6. _____
MY HEIGHT AND WEIGHT

7. _____
NUMBER OF PEOPLE IN MY FAMILY

I CAN COUNT UP TO

8. _____

Frog School

At Frog School, Croaker Frog and his friends sit on lily pads.

Are there enough lily pads for all the frogs in Croaker's class?
Yes ____   No ____

Draw lines to match the frogs with the lily pads.

How many frogs need lily pads? _____.

Scholastic Professional Books

Odd and Even Patterns

A pattern can have two things repeating. This is called an "AB" pattern.

1. Look around the classroom. What "AB" patterns do you see? Draw one "AB" pattern in the box.

2. Use red and blue crayons to color the numbers in the chart using an "AB" pattern.

Hundred's Chart

1	2	3	4	5	6	7	8	9	10
11	12	13	14	15	16	17	18	19	20
21	22	23	24	25	26	27	28	29	30
31	32	33	34	35	36	37	38	39	40
41	42	43	44	45	46	47	48	49	50
51	52	53	54	55	56	57	58	59	60
61	62	63	64	65	66	67	68	69	70
71	72	73	74	75	76	77	78	79	80
81	82	83	84	85	86	87	88	89	90
91	92	93	94	95	96	97	98	99	100

Use this rule:
1 = red
2 = blue
3 = red
4 = blue, and so on

The blue numbers are **even numbers**. They can be split evenly into 2 whole numbers.

The red numbers are **odd numbers**. They cannot be split evenly into 2 whole numbers.

Classroom Garage Sale

Tolu's class did some spring cleaning. Then they had a garage sale. They sorted the things they were selling. Sort these objects into like groups. Draw the items of each group on one of the tables below.

_____   _____   _____

Below each table, write a label for the group.

Flowers in a Pot

Count the dots in the boxes. Then color the matching number word.

■ green   □ yellow

■ red   ■ purple

■ blue

Use bright colors to draw a pot of flowers on another sheet of paper.

Sign Shape

Street signs come in different shapes. Use string to form the shapes below. Work with a partner. Answer the questions below about the shapes, too.

YIELD

What shape is this sign? _____

How many sides does it have? _____

CAUTION

What shape is this sign? _____

How many sides does it have? _____

SPEED LIMIT 35

What shape is this sign? _____

How many sides does it have? _____

STOP

What shape is this sign? _____

How many sides does it have? _____

Bird Feeder Geometry

It's spring! The birds are coming back. Kwaku and his mother made two bird feeders.

What shapes can you find on their feeders? Write your ideas on

the lines. _____

_____

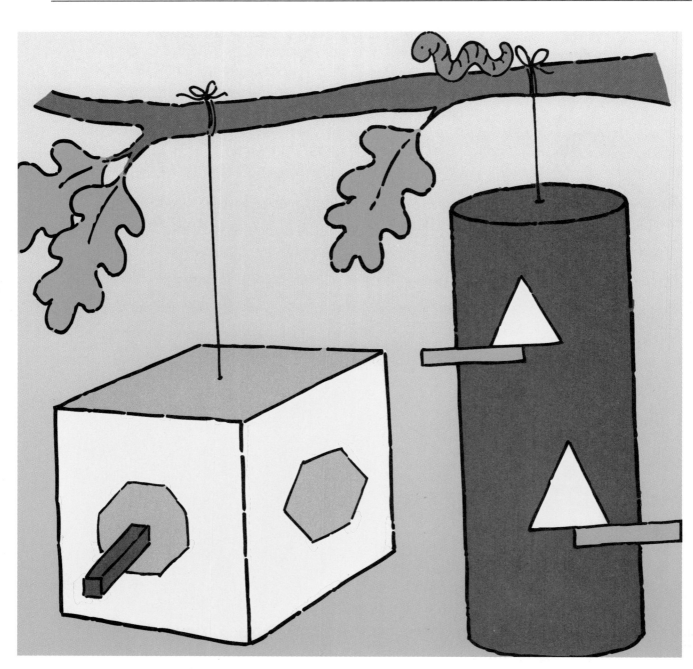

Shape Study

"Symmetry" exists when the two halves of something are mirror images of each other.

Look at the pictures below. Color those that show symmetry.
(Hint: Imagine the pictures are folded on the dotted lines.)

Complete the drawings below. Connect the dots to show the other half. (Hint: The pictures are symmetrical!)

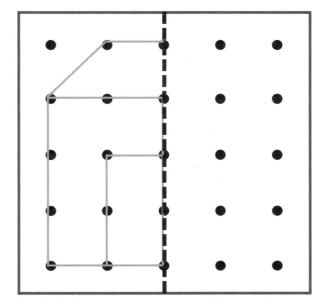

Picking Out Patterns

On the 100th day of school, everyone in Pat's class picked out patterns on the 100 Chart. Look at the chart below.

1	2	3	4	5	6	7	8	9	10
11	12	13	14	15	16	17	18	19	20
21	22	23	24	25	26	27	28	29	30
31	32	33	34	35	36	37	38	39	40
41	42	43	44	45	46	47	48	49	50
51	52	53	54	55	56	57	58	59	60
61	62	63	64	65	66	67	68	69	70
71	72	73	74	75	76	77	78	79	80
81	82	83	84	85	86	87	88	89	90
91	92	93	94	95	96	97	98	99	100

Find and finish the pattern starting with 2, 12, 22

_____

Find and finish the pattern starting with 100, 90, 80

_____

Find and finish the pattern starting with 97, 87, 77

_____

Find and finish the pattern starting with 11, 22, 33

_____

Mystery Critter

I climb up the side of walls and never fall.

I am a fast runner and have a very long tail. Who am I? _____

To find out, connect the numbers in order from 20 to 68.

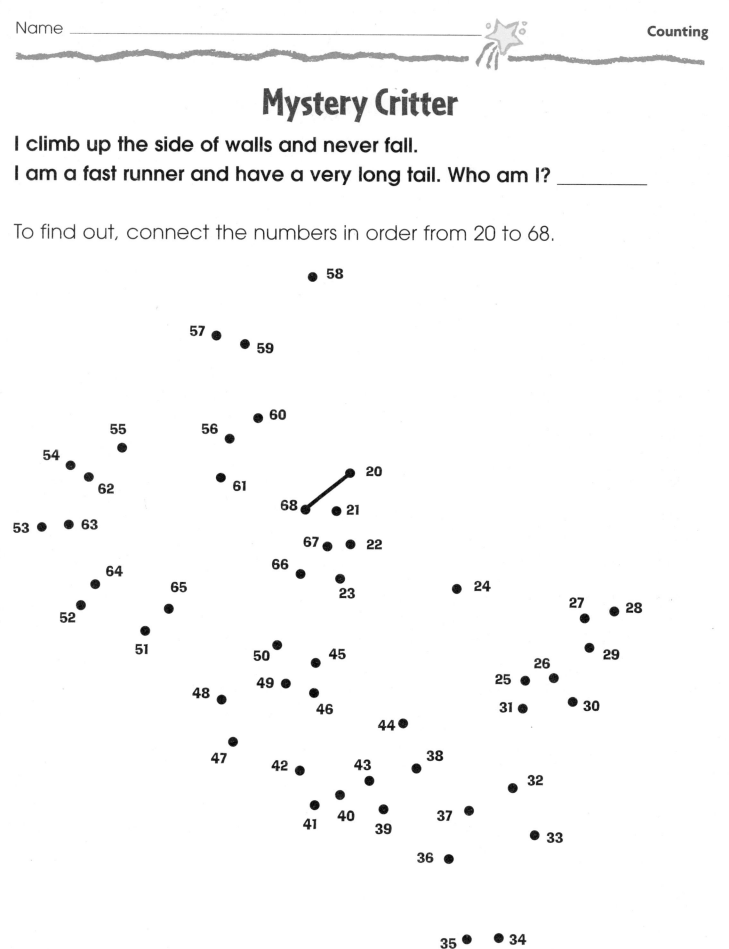

Snowflakes on Mittens

Estimate how many snowflakes are on each mitten.
For the first mitten, skip count by 2s to find out.
(You can circle groups of 2.)
For the second mitten, skip count by 5s to check your answer.
(You can circle groups of 5.)

 Would snowflakes really wait for you to count?

Explain your answer:

Patterns of Five

Look at the number chart below. Starting with 1, count 5 squares. Color in the fifth square. Then count 5 more squares and color in the fifth square. Keep going until you reach 100.

Hundred's Chart

1	2	3	4	5	6	7	8	9	10
11	12	13	14	15	16	17	18	19	20
21	22	23	24	25	26	27	28	29	30
31	32	33	34	35	36	37	38	39	40
41	42	43	44	45	46	47	48	49	50
51	52	53	54	55	56	57	58	59	60
61	62	63	64	65	66	67	68	69	70
71	72	73	74	75	76	77	78	79	80
81	82	83	84	85	86	87	88	89	90
91	92	93	94	95	96	97	98	99	100

Tally marks can be arranged in groups of five, like this: ⅢⅠ ⅢⅠ ⅢⅠ
Then you can count by fives.

Count how many girls and boys are in your class. Draw tally marks in groups of five.

Girls: _____   Boys: _____

Now count the total number. Write the totals here:

Girls: _____   Boys: _____

Ladybug Dots

Every year, ladybugs hibernate when the weather gets cool. Count the dots on each ladybug wing. Then write an equation to show the total number of dots each ladybug has. The first one has been done for you.

	__3__	+	__3__	=	__6__
	_____	+	_____	=	_____
	_____	+	_____	=	_____
	_____	+	_____	=	_____
	_____	+	_____	=	_____
	_____	+	_____	=	_____

Write the sums in order, from lowest to highest.

_____ _____ _____ _____ _____

What pattern do you see?

_____

Scholastic Professional Books

Pattern Block Design

How many total pieces are in this pattern block design?

2 + 2 + 1= _____

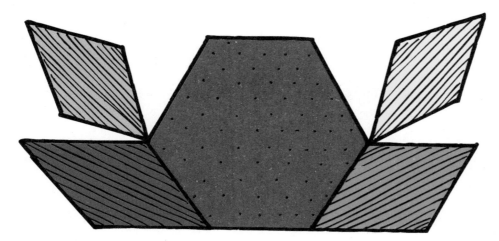

Now make your own design by drawing 5 pattern blocks. Connect the blocks to form a pattern different from the one above. You may want to use a block pattern more than once.

Write an equation to show how many of each shape you used.

Equation: _____

Coin-Toss Subtraction

Toss 3 coins. Write "H" for heads or "T" for tails in the circles below to show how the coins landed. Then finish each sentence to tell about your toss. Write a subtraction equation to show your toss, too. Write the number of heads first. We did the first one for you. Try it three times.

(H)(H)(T) There are ___more___ heads than tails.
                              (more/fewer)

Subtraction equation: ___3 coins___ - ___2 heads___ = ___1 tail___

( )( )( ) There are _____ heads than tails.
                              (more/fewer)

Subtraction equation: _____ - _____ = _____

( )( )( ) There are _____ heads than tails.
                              (more/fewer)

Subtraction equation: _____ - _____ = _____

( )( )( ) There are _____ heads than tails.
                              (more/fewer)

Subtraction equation: _____ - _____ = _____

What's Your Story?

Look at the equation below.

3 + 3 = 6

Make up a story to go with the equation.

Draw a picture in the box to go with your story.

Now write about your picture on the lines below.

_____

_____

_____

_____

_____

Coin-Toss Addition

Toss 6 coins. Write "H" for heads or "T" for tails in the circles below to show your toss. Then write the addition equation. Write the number of "heads" first. We did the first one for you. Try it five times.

(**H**) (**H**) (**H**) (**H**) (**T**) (**T**) Equation: **4 + 2 = 6** _____

◯ ◯ ◯ ◯ ◯ ◯ Equation: _____

◯ ◯ ◯ ◯ ◯ ◯ Equation: _____

◯ ◯ ◯ ◯ ◯ ◯ Equation: _____

◯ ◯ ◯ ◯ ◯ ◯ Equation: _____

◯ ◯ ◯ ◯ ◯ ◯ Equation: _____

Time to Get Up!

Twenty animals were hibernating near Sleepy Pond.
5 of them woke up. Color 5 animals below.

How many are still sleeping? _____

A week later, 7 more woke up. Color 7 other animals.

How many are still sleeping? _____

Money Matters

Alex asked his little brother Billy to trade piggy banks.

Alex's bank has these coins: Billy's has these coins:

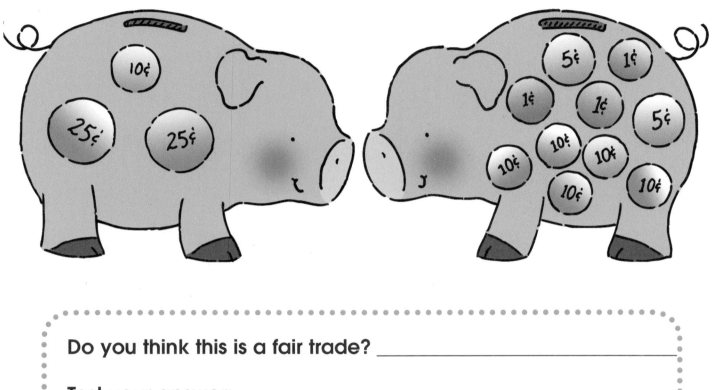

Do you think this is a fair trade? _____

Test your answer:

Add up Alex's coins: _____

Add up Billy's coins: _____

Write the totals in this Greater Than/Less Than equation:

_____ > _____

Who has more money? _____

The Truth About the Tooth Fairy

Look at Ali Gator's teeth.

	How many teeth?	How much money in all?
1. How many 1¢?		cents
2. How many 5¢?		cents
3. How many 10¢?		cents
4. How many 25¢?		cents

Measuring Up

People didn't always measure with rulers. Long ago, Egyptians and other peoples measured objects with body parts. Try it!

A "digit" is the width of your middle finger at the top joint where it bends.

How many digits long is:

a pair of scissors? _____

a math book? _____

a crayon? _____

A "palm" is the width of your palm.

How many palms long is:

a telephone book? _____

your desk? _____

a ruler? _____

A "span" is the length from the tip of your pinkie to the tip of your thumb when your hand is wide open.

How many spans long is:

a broom handle? _____

a table? _____

a door? _____

Scholastic Professional Books

Penguin Family on Parade

The penguin family is part of the winter parade. They need to line up from shortest to tallest. Give them a hand! Use a ruler to measure each penguin. Label each penguin with its height. Then write the name of each penguin in size order, from smallest to tallest.

Paul
Height:

_____

inches

Peter
Height:

_____

inches

Patty
Height:

_____

inches

Petunia
Height:

_____

inches

Size Order:

_____   _____   _____   _____

(smallest)   **(tallest)**

Look and Learn

Look at each picture. Estimate how long you think it is. Then measure each picture with a ruler. Write the actual length in inches.

Estimate: _____ inches
Actual: _____ inches

Estimate: _____ inches
Actual: _____ inches

Estimate: _____ inches
Actual: _____ inches

Estimate: _____ inches
Actual: _____ inches

Practice measuring other things in the room with a ruler.

Scholastic Professional Books

Turn Up the Volume

How many quarts equal 1 gallon? Find out! Fill a quart container with water. Pour it into a gallon container. Keep doing it until the gallon is full. Color the correct number of quarts below. Write the numeral on the line: **1 gallon = _____ quarts.**

Now try it with other containers, too.

1 quart = _____ pints

1 pint = _____ cups

1 cup = _____ tablespoons

 1 tablespoon = _____ teaspoons

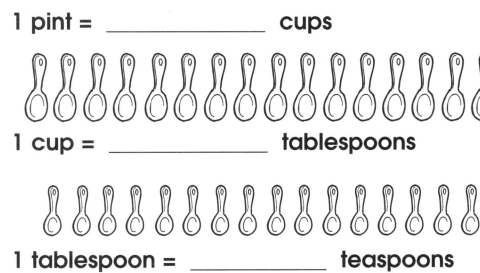

Adding Sides

Use the inch side of a ruler and measure each side of each rectangle. Write the inches in the spaces below. Then add up all the sides to find the perimeter, or distance, around each rectangle.

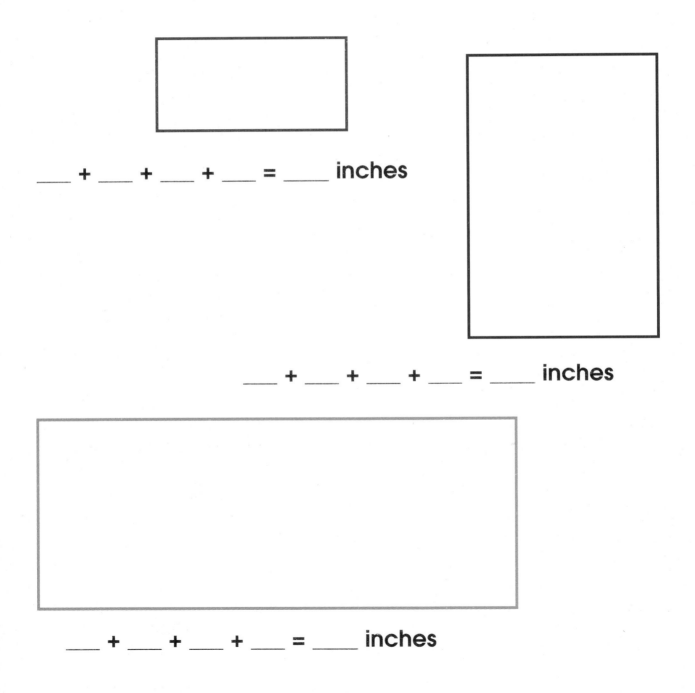

___ + ___ + ___ + ___ = ____ inches

___ + ___ + ___ + ___ = ____ inches

___ + ___ + ___ + ___ = ____ inches

Centimeters

Things can be measured using centimeters. Get a ruler that measures in centimeters. Measure the pictures of the objects below.

book

Out Came The Sun

_____ centimeters

book

By The River

_____ centimeters

straw

_____ centimeters

marker

_____ centimeters

5 cubes

_____ centimeters

10 cubes

_____ centimeters

shoe

_____ centimeters

hand

_____ centimeters

Five Senses

We learn about the world by using our 5 senses. The 5 senses are seeing, hearing, smelling, touching, and tasting.
Look at the pictures on the left side of the graph. Think about which of your senses you use to learn about it. Draw a checkmark in the box to show the senses used. (Hint: You might use more than one.)

Now graph how many senses you used for each object.

Rainbow Graph

Which color of the rainbow is your favorite? Color in the box for your favorite color. Have 5 classmates color the boxes to show their favorite colors, too.

Which color is liked the most? _____

Which color is liked the least? _____

Are any colors tied? _____

Which ones? _____

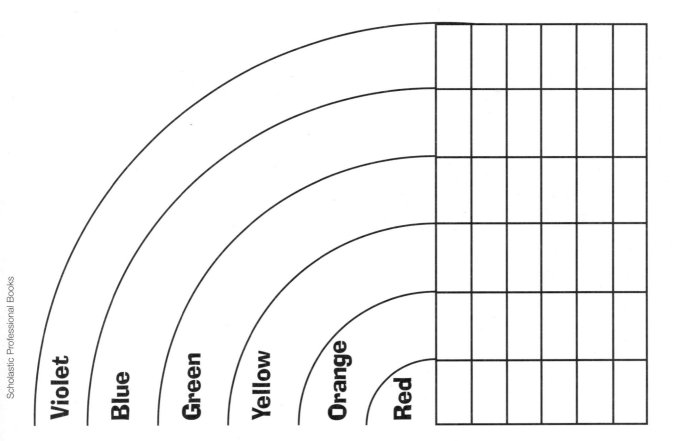

School Supplies

1. Find each letter and

   number pair on the graph.

2. Color a yellow square

   for each pair.

3. What picture did you make?

_____

	Across	Up
1.	C	4
2.	C	5
3.	D	4
4.	D	5
5.	E	4
6.	E	5
7.	F	4

	Across	Up
8.	F	5
9.	G	4
10.	G	5
11.	H	4
12.	H	5
13.	I	4
14.	I	5

Scholastic Professional Books

Surprises!

1. Find each number pair on the graph. Make a dot for each.

2. Connect the dots in the order that you make them.

3. What picture did you make?

_____

	Across	Up
1.	9	2
2.	7	4
3.	8	4
4.	6	6
5.	7	6
6.	5	8
7.	3	6
8.	4	6
9.	2	4
10.	3	4
11.	1	2

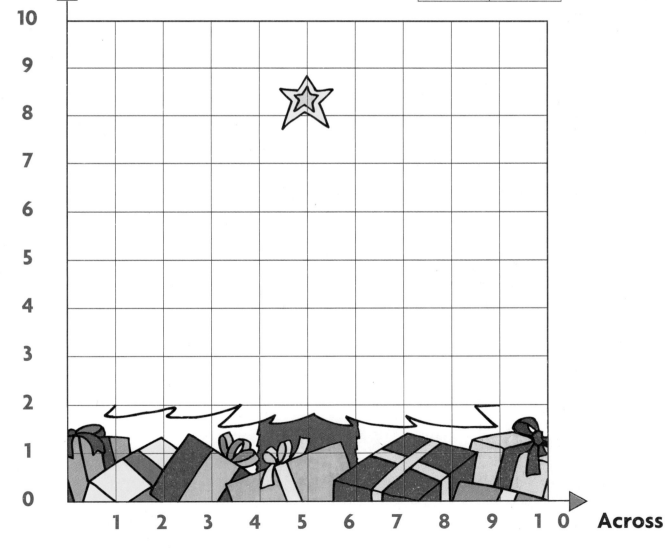

Up

10
9
8
7
6
5
4
3
2
1
0

1 2 3 4 5 6 7 8 9 1 0 **Across**

December Weather

In December, Mrs. Monroe's class drew the weather on a calendar.
Each kind of weather has a picture:

| sunny | cloudy | rainy | snowy |

Look at the calendar. Answer the questions below.

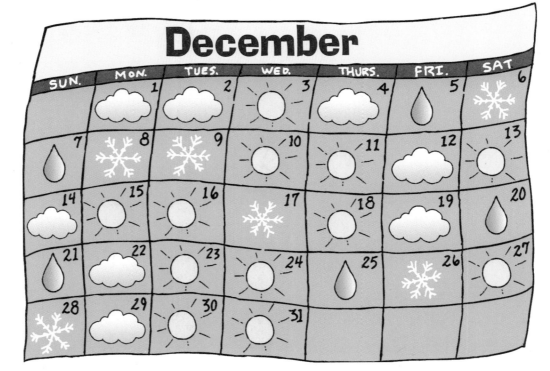

How many sunny days did they have? _____

How many cloudy days did they have? _____

How many rainy days did they have? _____

How many snowy days did they have? _____

Which kind of weather did they have the most? _____

Fun With Fractions

 A fraction is a part of a whole.

The shapes below are split into parts, or fractions.
Color only the shapes that are split into equal parts (equal fractions).

Parts to Color

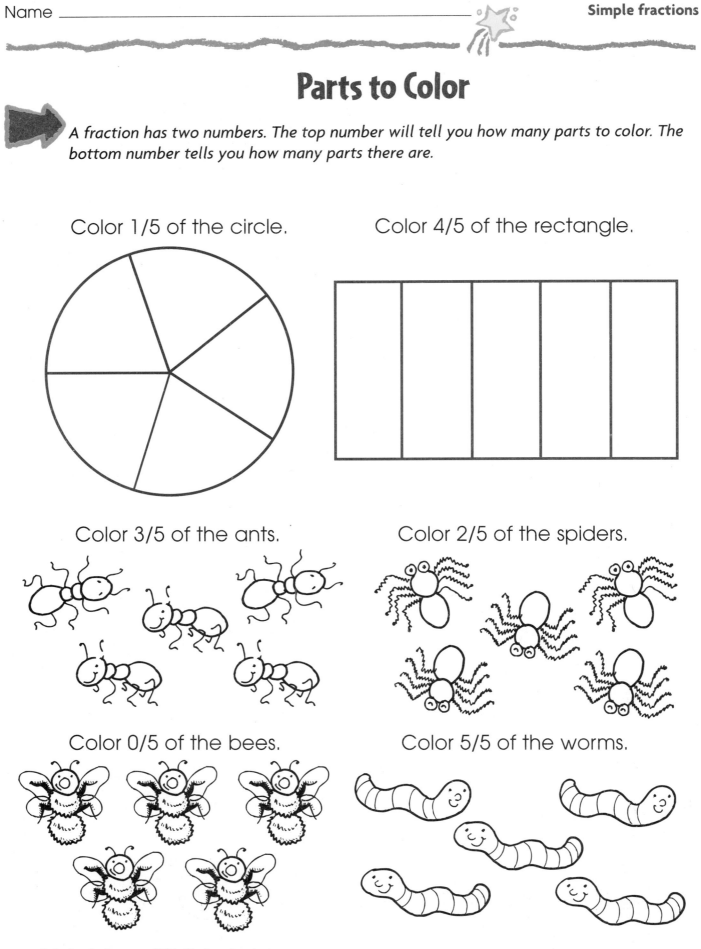

A fraction has two numbers. The top number will tell you how many parts to color. The bottom number tells you how many parts there are.

Color 1/5 of the circle.

Color 4/5 of the rectangle.

Color 3/5 of the ants.

Color 2/5 of the spiders.

Color 0/5 of the bees.

Color 5/5 of the worms.

More Parts to Color

A fraction has two numbers. The top number will tell you how many parts to color. The bottom number tells you how many parts there are.

Color 1/8 of the circle.

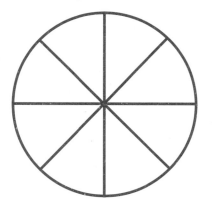

Color 6/8 of the rectangle.

Color 4/8 of the suns.   Color 8/8 of the stars.

Color 2/8 of the moons.   Color 3/8 of the planets.

Clock Work

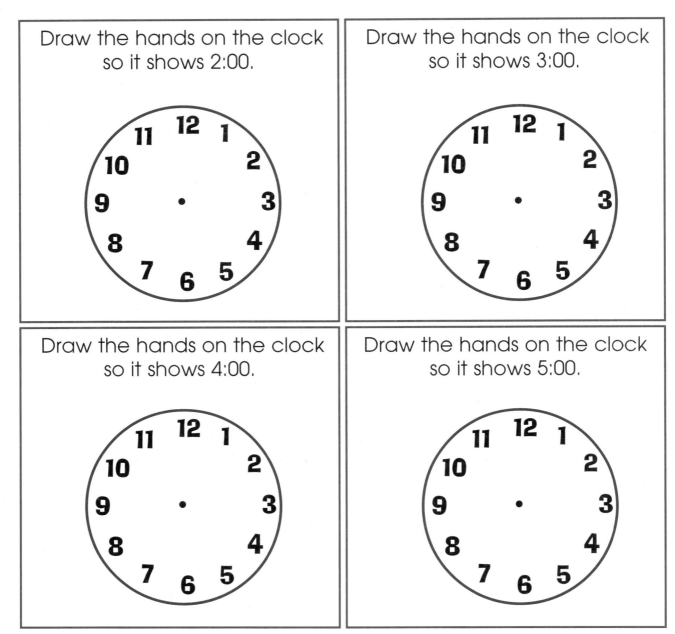

Draw the hands on the clock so it shows 2:00.

Draw the hands on the clock so it shows 3:00.

Draw the hands on the clock so it shows 4:00.

Draw the hands on the clock so it shows 5:00.

What do you do at 2:00 in the afternoon?

Write about it on the lines below.

_____

_____

More Clock Work

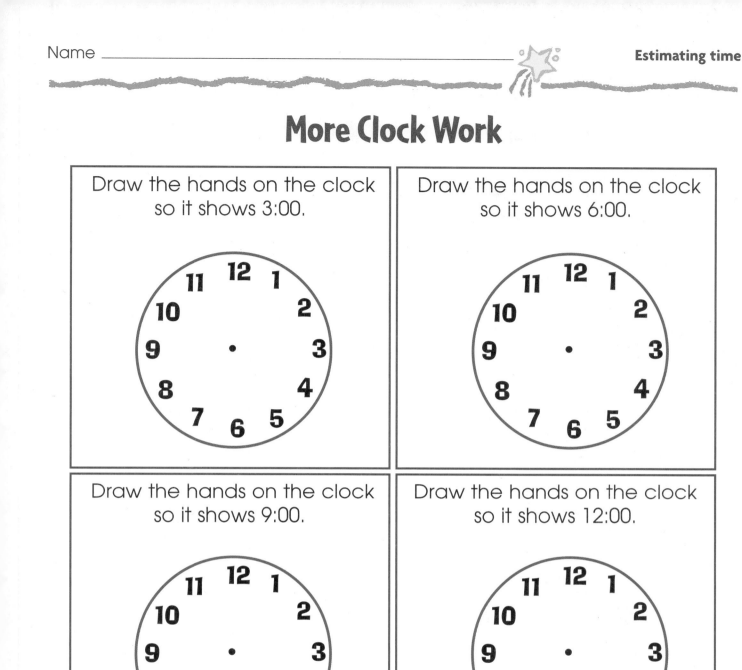

Draw the hands on the clock so it shows 3:00.

Draw the hands on the clock so it shows 6:00.

Draw the hands on the clock so it shows 9:00.

Draw the hands on the clock so it shows 12:00.

What do you do at 3:00 in the afternoon?

Write about it on the lines below.

_____

_____

Even More Clock Work

Draw the hands on the clock so it shows 4:00.

Draw the hands on the clock so it shows 4:30.

What do you do at 4:00 in the afternoon?

Write about it on the line below.

_____

Draw the hands on the clock so it shows 6:00.

Draw the hands on the clock so it shows 6:30.

What do you do at 6:00 in the evening?

Write about it on the line below.

_____

About Time

Why do we need to know how to tell time? List your ideas below.

_____

_____

_____

_____

How Long Is a Minute?

Think about how much you can do in one minute.
Write your estimates in the Prediction column. Then time yourself.
Write the actual number in the Result column.

Prediction: In One Minute I Can	**Result**
Jump rope _____ times.	
Write the numbers 1 to _____ .	
Say the names of _____ animals.	

Answer Key

READING COMPREHENSION

Page 12
1. a good reader; 2. looks at the picture; 3. the title; 4. the words

Page 13
Main idea: Trucks do important work.

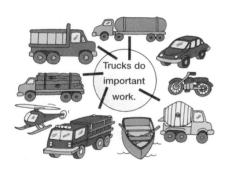

Page 14
Main idea: Clowns can do funny tricks.

Page 15
KATE: Names have special meanings.

Casey means brave.
George means farmer.
Sarah means princess.

Page 16

Page 17

1. in reading class; 2. camping

Page 18
Kelly packed pajamas, shirt, shorts, toothbrush, toothpaste, hairbrush, swimsuit, pillow, storybooks, sunglasses. Compound words: grandmother, suitcase, toothbrush, toothpaste, hairbrush, swimsuit, storybooks, sunglasses

Page 19
1. Texas; 2. oil; 3. President; 4. wife; 5. Jenna

His cat's name was INDIA.

Page 20
Make-believe: ketchup bottles and a watermelon bowling, a talking milk jug, dancing bananas, chicken wings that can fly all by themselves, laughing soup cans, dancing carrots

Page 21
Facts: Clouds float in the sky. Clouds are made of tiny drops of water. Fog is a cloud on the ground. (All others are make-believe.)

Page 22
Make-believe: pig, goat and sheep, horses, pizza and hamburgers, mouse and table, golden eggs, crickets (The others are real.)

Page 23
5, 1; 4, 3, 2
Tara bought pencils, scissors, glue, and crayons.

Page 24
6, 4, 2; 3, 1, 5
LEARN TO DIVE

Page 25
1. Each star should be outlined in blue and colored red inside. 2. One moon should be yellow and one orange. 3. A face should be drawn on each sun. 4. 3; 5. 2; 6. 4; 7. 3 + 2 + 4 = 9; 8. stars and moon

Page 26

Page 27

The pictures that do not belong are bike, telephone, snowman, pumpkin, skates, and frog. (The other pictures should be colored.)

2. hot, cold; 3. up, down; 4. starfish; 5. yellow

Page 28

IT WAS A FLYING CARPET. No

Page 29

1. true; 2. false; 3. false; 4. true; 5. true

Page 30

The children's pictures should include everything described in the sentences.

Page 31

The children should have added these things to the picture: black clouds, lightning striking the tallest tree, the word "Moo" in a bubble above a cow, rain, a mud puddle by the barn door, hay blowing out of the barn window.

Page 32

1. penguin; 2. baby; 3. octopus; 4. ant; 5. grandmother; 6. bear; 7. firefighter

Page 33

1. head cold; 2. The children sneezed. 3. 9; 4. She got a cold, too.

Page 34

Page 35

Bacon and eggs do not belong.

Page 36

Sandie's Shoe Store: sandals, boots, sneakers, high heels; Movie Town Cinema: tickets, popcorn, big screen, candy; Pepe's Mexican Food: tacos, burrito, beans, peppers; Gale's Gardening Goodies: tulip bulbs, fertilizer, gardening gloves, pots

Page 37

Answers will vary.

Page 38

Page 39

He knew he had to do the right thing.

Page 40

FAST FOOD, FLOWER BED

Page 41

They are in the first grade.

Scholastic Professional Books

Page 42

1. Juan's dad; 2. Juan's dad;
3. both; 4. Ann's dad; 5. both;
6. Ann's dad; 7. Juan's dad; 8. both;
9. Ann's dad; 10. both

Page 43

1.

2.

3.

Page 44

1. an arm like a paddle; 2. not
dangerous; 3. slap at; 4. lose;
5. hide in the ground

Page 45

1. a small city; 2. little furry animals;
3. tunnels; 4. rooms; 5. pests

Page 46

1. Sandy used lanterns at night
because the cabin had no electricity.
2. Sandy and Austin bathed in a
stream because the cabin had no
running water. 3. Sandy felt better
about missing Kendra because she
talked to her on the cell phone. 4.
Sandy's dad could not call his office
because the cell phone was dead.

Page 47

1. The worms got tangled up when
they danced. 2. They were tied in a
knot so they got married.

Page 48

1. E; 2. B; 3. D; 4. F; 5. A; 6. C.

Page 49

The children's pictures should show
a crown on Margie's arm, a shoe on
her head, different colors on each
fingernail, a red nose, a fork in her
hair, and a purple belt around her
knees.

6. the way she dresses; 7. He wears
his clothes backward.

Page 50

1. happy; 2. worried; 3. silly; 4. sad;
5. scared; 6. surprised

Page 51

1. green; 2. red; 3. red; 4. yellow;
5. red; 6. yellow; 7. green

Page 52

Picture: rainbow 1. appear; 2. gold;
Picture: airplane 3. high; 4. again;
5. bee

Page 53

2. Don't be greedy. Be happy with
what you have. Picture answers: dog,
meat, bridge

Page 54

1. sharing 2. Marcus Pfister

TESTS: READING

Pages 57-60

TEST 1

**A. Phonic Analysis: Consonants
   and Vowels**

Sample: sun

1. bed   2. cat   3. dog
4. rug   5. sock

**B. Vocabulary:
   Picture-Word Match**

Sample: can

1. pig   2. run   3. car

C. High-Frequency Word Match

Sample: and

1. my   2. will   3. sad

**D. Grammar, Usage, and
   Mechanic's**

Sample: My bike is red.

1. I like to run.

2. Did you see it?

3. They sit on the mat.

E. Reading Sentences

Sample: A girl sits.

1. The cat plays.

2. The book is on the desk.

3. She has a rabbit.

4. The dog sits on a hill.

F. Story Comprehension

1. dog

2. Rags the Dog

3. play

Pages 61-64

Test 2

A. Phonic Analysis:
   Consonants

Sample: bat

1. pot 2. fox 3. bell

4. bus 5. bug

B. Phonic Analysis: Vowels

Sample: cap

1. mop 2. pig 3. sun

4. duck 5. ten

C. High-Frequency
   Word Match

Sample: and

1. it 2. she 3. was

4. that 5. they

D. Vocabulary: Picture-Word
   Match

Sample: hat

1. bag 2. top 3. pen

4. fan 5. sock

E. Grammar, Usage,
   and Mechanics

Sample: The boy is happy.

1. She saw a duck.

2. Look at him run!

3. Where will I go?

F. Story Comprehension

1. a pig

2. Ted's Pig

3. Answers will vary.

Pages 65-68

Test 3

A. Phonic Analysis:
   Consonants

Sample: sun

1. ball 2. rug 3. flag

4. pen 5. truck

B. Phonic Analysis: Vowels

Sample: fish

1. bus 2. hat 3. frog

4. nest 5. cake

C. High-Frequency
   Word Match

Sample: is

1. for 2. he 3. you

4. said 5. them

D. Vocabulary:
   Picture-Word Match

Sample: bird

1. bat 2. dog 3. feet

4. hand 5. clock

E. Grammar, Usage,
   and Mechanics

Sample: The girl can jump.

1. The boy ran fast.

2. Look at me!

3. Where will I walk?

F. Story Comprehension

1. a kite

2. Kim's Kite

3. Answers will vary.

Pages 69-72

Test 4

A. Phonic Analysis:
   Consonants

Sample: dog

1. bat 2. fan 3. tree

4. moon 5. fish

B. Phonic Analysis: Vowels

Sample:sun

1.map 2.web 3.fox

4.pig 5.cake

C. High-Frequency
   Word Match

Sample: and

1. for 2. she 3. how

4. can 5. then

D. Vocabulary:
   Picture-Word Match

Sample: pen

1. hat 2. frog 3. bus

4. feet 5. bike

E. Grammar, Usage,
   and Mechanics

Sample: The

1. She

2. They

3. out!

4. day?

5. Amy.

6. I

7. We

8. his

9. Anna and Tim

F. Story Comprehension
1. a cat
2. string
3. Nate's Cat
4. Answers will vary

.

Pages 73-76

Test 5

A. Phonic Analysis: Consonants
Sample: baby
1. sheep   2. bath   3. snail
4. tree   5. frog

B. Phonic Analysis: Vowels
Sample: car
1. spoon   2. legs
3. puppies   4. boy   5. milk

C. High-Frequency Word Match
Sample: is
1. to   2. said   3. hello
4. best   5. smell

D. Vocabulary:
  Picture-Word Match
Sample: ant
1. wet   2. dish   3. saw
4. bug   5. cake

E. Grammar, Usage,
  and Mechanics
Sample: is
1. I
2. The
3. me!
4. Nan and Nell
5. you
6. We
7. They
8. Joey.
9. She

F. Story Comprehension
1. goldfish
2. Goldie and Finny
3. bowl

Pages 77-80

Test 6

A. Phonic Analysis: Consonants
Sample: bag
1. mop   2. cheese   3. ten
4. fish   5. train

B. Phonic Analysis: Vowels
Sample: sun
1. six   2. cat   3. boat
4. teeth   5. foot

C. High-Frequency
  Word Match
Sample: me
1. is   2. said   3. where

D. Grammar, Usage, and
  Mechanics
Sample: The dog is furry.
1. He didn't like it.
2. Can you run fast?
3. Where can I play?

E. Reading Sentences
Sample: A boy runs.
1. She put the sock in the box.
2. The nest has ten eggs.
3. She plays on the swing.
4. The truck can go fast.

F. Story Comprehension
1. read
2. Books Tom Reads
3. animals
4. Pet Rabbits

Pages 81-84

Test 7

A. Phonic Analysis: Consonants
Sample: fish
1. pen   2. broom   3. nest
4. truck   5. cheese

B. Phonic Analysis: Vowels
Sample: bat
1. ten   2. house   3. leaf
4. book   5. plane

C. High-Frequency
  Word Match
Sample: and
1. has   2. come   3. what

D. Grammar, Usage,
  and Mechanics
Sample: The cat sleeps.
1. Why can't we go?
2. They play all day.
3. Can Sam sit with us?

E. Reading Sentences
Sample: The boy kicks the ball.
1. The duck swims in the pond.
2. She rides her bike.
3. The leaf fell off the branch.
4. He can see the cow.

F. Story Comprehension
1. The Wind.
2. to fly a kite
3. seeds grow
4. blow away a leaf

Pages 85-88

Test 8

A. Phonic Analysis: Consonants

Sample: desk

1. pan 2. tree 3. ship

4. clock 5. hand

B. Phonic Analysis

Sample: net

1. cup 2. moon 3. cloud

4. boat 5. rake

C. Vocabulary: Picture-Word Match

Sample: fish

1. bed 2. nest 3. plane

4. coat 5. kite

D. High-Frequency Word Match

Sample: in

1. him 2. then 3. says

4. our 5. what

E. Grammar, Usage and Mechanics

Sample: He rides in a plane.

1. She runs very fast.

2. Where are my socks?

3. We play with the dog.

F. Story Comprehension

1. Rabbits

2. hear sounds from far away

3. in holes in the ground and in people's homes

4. Answers will vary.

Pages 89-92

Test 9

A. Phonic Analysis: Consonants

Sample: dress

1. train 2. flag 3. lamp

4. desk 5. spoon

B. Phonic Analysis: Vowels

Sample: fox

1. bell 2. gate 3. hose

4. teeth 5. leaf

C. High-Frequency Word Match

Sample: her

1. very 2. some 3. there

4. which 5. because

D. Vocabulary: Picture-Word Match

Sample: frog

1. kite 2. fish 3. plane

4. cupcake 5. butterfly

E. Grammar, Usage, and Mechanics

Sample: We

1. jump. 2. Dr. Jones 3. I

4. New York 5. rides

F. Story Comprehension

1. Jane Goodall

2. Africa

3. 3 years old

4. Answers will vary

Pages 93-96

Test 10

A. Phonic Analysis: Consonants

Sample: dog

1. six 2. tree 3. top

4. fan 5. ship

B. Phonic Analysis: Vowels

Sample: hat

1. sock 2. sun 3. coat

4. train 5. bike

C. High Frequency Word Match

Sample: the

1. is 2. have 3. said

D. Grammar, Usage, and Mechanics

Sample: The boy is happy.

1. She can't help us.

2. Can we play ball?

3. Where will I go?

E. Reading Sentences

Sample: A girl runs.

1. He walks the dog.

2. I can sit next to you.

3. The man has a big hat.

4. I like to play games.

F. Story Comprehension

1. dogs and cats

2. Good Pets

3. run and jump

Pages 97-100

Test 11

A. Phonic Analysis: Consonants

Sample: door

1. plant 2. twelve

3. thumb 4. sneakers

5. bench

B. Phonic Analysis: Vowels

Sample: girl

1. mouse 2. game

3. button 4. skates 5. egg

C. High-Frequency Word Match

Sample: send

1. that 2. like 3. sit

4. of 5. book

D. Vocabulary: Picture-Word Match

Sample: jump

1. brush 2. friends 3. pants

4. dollar 5. nine

E. Grammar, Usage, and Mechanics

Sample: eats

1. My 2. lives 3. is

4. Do 5. have 6. They

F. Story Comprehension

1. Baby Penguins

2. three days

3. the mother and father

4. Answers will vary.

GRAMMAR

Page 148
1. The 2. The 3. The 4. The

Page 149
1. The cat sat. 2. The dog sat.
3. I see the cat. 4. I can see.

Page 150
1. The 2. My 3. Jan 4. I 5. Ants

Page 151
1. I see Jan⊙ 2. I go with Jan⊙
3. We see Dan⊙
4. I go with Dan and Jan⊙
5. school. 6. school.

Page 152
1. Dan is in the cab.
2. The cat is in the cab.
3. Mom is in the cab.
4. We see Dan and Mom.
5. van.   6. red.

Page 153
1. The cat is on the mat.
2. The rat is on the mop.
3. The rat sees the cat.
4. The rat can hop.
5. The cat and rat sit.

Page 154
1. Ⓘ like to hop.
2. Pam and Ⓘ like to hop.
3. Ⓘ can hop to Mom.
4. Mom and Ⓘ can hop.
5. Answers will vary.

Page 155
1. I 2. I 3. I 4. I
5. Answers will vary.

Page 156
1. I sit on a mat. 2. Pam and I like cats. 3. I see the van. 4. I like jam.
5. I like to nap.

Page 157
1. Pam 2. Dan 3. The cat
4. The van
5. Jan is hot.
6. The hat is on top.
7. The man sat.

Page 158
1. Bill paints. 2. Tom likes to read.
3. Pat plants flowers.
4. Answers will vary.

Page 159
1. The cat sits on a mat. 2. Pam and Dan like jam. 3. I see Mom.
4. I like my hat. 5. Ben can hop.

Page 160
1. I 2. Pam 3. We 4. We
1. I like dots.
2. Pam likes dots.
3. We like hats.
4. We like hats with dots.

Page 161
1. I like cats. 2. I see a man.
3. We go to school

Page 162
1. I see red dots. 2. Dan is in a big van. 3. The cat is fat. 4. We like the hat. 5. Ben likes jam.

Page 163
1. ⑦ 2. ⑦ 3. ⑦ 4. ⑦
5. Answers will vary.
6. Answers will vary.

Page 164
1. Who hid the cat⑦
2. Can the cat see the rat⑦
4. Can the van go⑦
5. Can we sit in the van?
6. Can Dan nap in the van?

Page 165
1. Who hid my hat?
2. Did the hat have dots?
3. Did Jan like my hat?
4. Can you see the hat?
5. Dan has the hat?

Page 166
1. pig 2. pan 3. Pam 4. you, hill
5. The sun is hot.
6. Sam ran and ran.
7. Is the cat fat?

Page 167
1. Al, van 2. cat, mat 3. Pat, hill
4. Dan, Jan

Page 168
1. c. 2. b 3. b 4. a 5. c

Page 169
1. Ⓗill Ⓟark 2. Ⓟam 3. Ⓓon
4. Ⓕrog Ⓛake 5. Answers will vary.

Page 170
1. Pam. 2. Ant Hill 3. Ron
4. Bat Lake 5. Spot 6. Hill Street

Page 171
1. Don 2. Pig Hill 3. Jam Street
4. Jan 5. Ham Lake

Page 172
1. sits 2. ran 3. hid 4. naps 5. run
6. see

Page 173
1. see 2. sits 3. mops 4. run
5. hops

Page 174
1. b 2. a 3. c 4. c 5. a

Page 175
1. big 2. fast 3. bad 4. fat
5. fat 6. little

Page 176
1. little, fast
2. hot, big
3. It is fat.
4. They are little.

Page 177
1. silly 2. bad 3. black 4. big
5. green

Page 178
1. (I,) 2. (T,) 3. (H). 4. (T,)
5. I can fill the basket.
7. We can clean.

Page 179
1. She has a mop.
2. The dog is on top.
3. Dan gets the hats.
4. Ron can clean spots.
5. (P)ut it in the pot(.)

Page 180
1. You can get it.
2. The basket is big.
3. The hat is in the basket.
4. A cat can not go in it.
5. We can fill the basket.

Page 181
1. Help(!) The rat is on top(!)
2. Get the cat(!)
3. This cat is bad(!)
4. Uh-oh(!) The cat is wet(!)
5. Oh my! Get the dog!
6. Oh! The dog runs!

Page 182
1. Run to the show!
2. Oh my, I'm very late!
3. What a great show!
4. Watch out, the floor is wet!
5. Wow, we had lots of fun!

Page 183
1. Yes! The cow can kick!
2. That cat is bad!
3. That rat runs fast!
4. Oh no! A frog is in my house!
5. The pot is hot!

Page 184
1. hats 2. eggs 3. girls 4. cats
5. mugs 6. hands

Page 185
1. Jan has her mittens.
2. She will run up hills.
3. Jan runs with her dogs.
4. The dogs can jump.
5. cats 6. socks

Page 186
1. hands 2. pots 3. dogs 4. ants
5. frogs

Page 187
1. sits 2. sees 3. digs 4. naps
5. sees 6. run

Page 188
1. play 2. dance 3. talk 4. run

Page 189
1. sits 2. naps 3. hops
4. digs 5. ran

Page 190
1. We; school 2. ball 3. girl
4. friends
Person: girl Place: school
Thing: ball

Page 191
1. Run and kick
   in the (park.)
2. Kick with a (foot.)
3. Kick the (ball.)
4. The (girl) will run
   to get it.
5. Kick it to the (net.)

Page 192
1. park 2. girl 3. ball 4. friend
5. net

Page 193
1. The king is sad.
2. Let's bake him a cake.
3. Tell the king to come.
4. Let's eat the cake.
The king eats.

Page 194

1. This bear likes snow.
2. The water is cold.
3. The bear runs fast.
4. Two bears play.

Page 195

1. Pam will bake a cake.
2. Pam will see the king.
3. The king has a duck.
4. The duck is in the lake.
5. The king will eat cake.

Page 196

circle: What, See, Night, The, Light, Moon, See, Many, Stars, The, Sun, Moon

Answers will vary.

Page 197

1. look, stars 2. the, moon, shines, night 3. we, see, planets 4. many, moons, shine 5. night, day 6. The Sun in the Sky 7. See the Stars!

Page 198

1. Where Is the Sun? 2. Many Cats to See 3. Day and Night 4. How Many Pigs? 5. The Big, Bad Wolf

Page 199

1. pot 2. pan 3. top 4. Jim
5. The pot is hot. —
6. See the pan? —
7. Jim is fast. —

Page 200

1. Jan, van 2. van 3. van, hill
4. Dan, Jan 5. answers will vary

Page 201

1. pans 2. Jim 3. cat 4. rat 5. cat

Page 202

1. is 2. were 3. was 4. are 5. now
6. in the past 7. now

Page 203

1. are, now 2. is, now 3. was, past
4. is, now 5. were, past

Page 204

1. was 2. were 3. are 4. is 5. are

Page 205

1. The, Gruff 2. They, Troll 3. His, Nosey 4. He 5. Dan and Pam like the play. Names a person, place, or thing. 6. They will read it to Jim. First word in a sentence.

Page 206

1. Raul 2. Mrs. Chin 3. Sue
4. Lee Park

Page 207

1. I   2. Ron 3. Gruff 4. Troll
5. Nosey

WRITING

Page 210

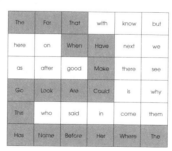

Page 211

1. The mouse; 2. He finds;
3. He eats; 4. Then he; 5. Oh no,;
6. The mouse

Page 212

1. We read; 2. Then we; 3. My bed;
4. My cat; 5. The sky; 6. My eyes

Page 213

1. My dog; 2. She must; 3. Maybe she; 4. Sometimes she; 5. I think

Page 214

Check that the child has added a period to the end of each sentence.

Page 215

Check that the child has added a period to the end of each sentence.

Page 216

1. Frogs and toads lay eggs.
2. The eggs are in the water.
3. Tadpoles hatch from the eggs.
4. The tadpoles grow legs.
5. The tadpoles lose their tails.

Page 217

1. Tadpoles become frogs or toads.
2. Frogs live near water. 3. Toads live mostly on dry land. 4. Frogs have wet skin. 5. Toads have bumpy skin.

Page 218

The following sentences should be colored red: This is a flag., The flag has stars., The stars are white., The stripes are red., The stripes are white., The flag has a blue part., There are 50 stars.; The rest are not sentences and should be colored white.

Page 219

Page 220
Five boats are sailing.; We have four buckets.

Page 221
A jaguar is hiding.; Some butterflies are blue.; Frogs jump in the water.; Green snakes hang from trees.; The trees grow very tall.

Page 222
The snakes on the left side of the page should have been colored.

Page 223
1. The blue snake;
2. The yellow snake;
3. The green snake;
4. The brown snake;
5. The red snake; 6. The purple snake; 7. The black snake; 8. The orange snake

Page 224
Sentences will vary.

Page 225
Sentences will vary.

Page 226
Sentences will vary.

Page 227
Sentences will vary.

Page 228
The bones on the right side of the page should have been colored.

Page 229
1. is jumping.; 2. is barking.; 3. is eating.; 4. is sleeping.

Page 230
Sentences will vary.

Page 231
Answers will vary.

Page 232
Sentences will vary.

Page 233
Sentences will vary.

Page 234
Pictures will vary.

Page 235
Answers will vary.

Page 236
1. long ago; 2. yesterday; 3. in winter;
4. today; 5. in the fall; 6. last night;
7. all day; 8. at noon;
9. yesterday; 10. on Thanksgiving Day; 11. this morning; 12. Tomorrow

Page 237
Sentences will vary.

Page 238
Answers will vary.

Page 239
Sentences will vary.

Page 240
Sentences will vary.

Page 241
Sentences will vary.

Page 242
kitten, bat, cracker, ball

Page 243
sweet, red, smooth; bumpy, salty, crunchy,; small, squeaky, furry

Page 244
Adjectives will vary.

Page 245
Sentences will vary.

Page 246
Sentences will vary.

Page 247
Sentences will vary.

Page 248
Sentences will vary.

Page 249
Sentences will vary.

Page 250
My Space Friend; A Big Beak; The Big Win; A Knight's Tale

Page 251
Stories will vary.

Page 252
Sentences will vary.

Page 253
Sentences and pictures will vary.

MAPS

Page 256
1. yes
2. yes
3. yes
4. no
5. swimming pool; car; lawn

Page 257
Child should color answers on map.

Page 258
4. truck
5. yes

Page 259
Child should color answers on map.

Page 261
1. far
2. near
3. above
4. right
5. left

Pages 262–263
1. yes
2. yes
3. no
4. yes
5. school
6. flower shop
7. Map 3
8. Map 1

Page 264
1. round
2. people, animals, plants
3. Drawings will vary.

Page 265
1. blue, green, orange, yellow, purple, red
2. blue
3. smaller

Page 266
1. south
2. east

Page 267
1. east
2. north
3. west
4. south

Page 268
1. north
2. east
3. north
4. west

Page 269
1–4 Line begins at gate, runs north to popcorn, west to Ferris wheel, east to face painting, west to popcorn and north to arcade.
5. south

Page 270
1. c.   2. a.   3. d.   4. b.

Page 271
1. tree
2. airplane
3. railroad track
4. beach umbrella

Page 272
1. garden
2. road
3. house
4. stable

Page 273
1. south
2. sheep
3. west
4. Tree symbol should be drawn for forest.

Pages 274–275
1. mountain
2. plain
3. hill
4. river
5. mountain
6. hill
7. lake

Page 276
1–4 Child should write answers on picture.

Page 277
1. plain
2. east
3. west
4. Answers will vary.

Page 278
1. hill
2. campground
3. picnic table
4. river or lake
5. west

Page 279
1. Doony Park
2. snack stand
3. a fountain
4. dog run
5. playground
6. west

Page 280
1. school
2. apartment
3. store
4. house
5. Drawings will vary.

Page 281
1. school
2. Spring Street
3. Summer Street
4. west

Page 282
1. South Street
2. West Street
3. North Street
4. South Street

Page 283
1. Routes will vary.
2. East Street
4. west
5. north

Page 285
1. border
2. road
3. a river
4. south
5. west

Page 287
1. state border
2. Answers will vary.
3. Answers will vary.
4. Answers will vary.
5. south

6. west
7. Arizona
8. Indiana

Page 288
1. state capital
2. south
3. north
4. west

Page 289
1. state border
2. Ohio River
3. Wabash River
4. four
5. Lake Michigan

Page 290
1. south
2. Answers will vary.
3. west
4. east
5. Answers will vary.

Page 292
1. country border
2. Canada
3. south

Page 293
1. Atlantic Ocean
2. Pacific Ocean

Pages 294–295
2. Atlantic, Pacific, Arctic, Indian, Southern
3. Europe
4. South America
5. Indian Ocean
6. Arctic Ocean
7. Antarctica

Page 296
1. pond
2. hill
3. North Street
4. Routes will vary.
5. post office on South Street
6. north

Page 297
1. states
2. Raleigh
3. plains
4. four
5. Atlantic Ocean
6. west

Page 298
1. south
2. lake
3. border
4. symbol
5. mountain
6. route
Secret Words: United States

ADDITION & SUBTRACTION
Page 302

Check child's coloring.

Page 303

1 + 2 = 3, 2 + 3 = 5, 7 + 3 = 10; 3 + 4 = 7, 1 + 0 = 1, 3 + 2 = 5; 1 + 1 = 2, 4 + 4 = 8; 1 + 3 = 4; The ladybug with 10 spots should be colored red. The ladybug with 1 spot should be colored blue.

Page 304

Check that the child has drawn the correct number of flowers. 7: needs 3, 10: needs 5, 4: needs 1; 6: needs 2, 9: needs 5; 5: needs 3, 8: needs 4, 3: needs 2; Color the bows with the numbers 4, 6, 8, and 10 yellow. Color the bows with 3, 5, 7, and 9 purple.

Page 305

A SAXOPHONE

6 + 2 = 8; 5 + 1 = 6; 4 + 4 = 8

3 + 6 = 9; 3 + 0 = 3; 3 + 4 = 7

2 + 2 = 4; 2 + 1 = 3; 1 + 1 = 2

0 + 1 = 1

Page 306

5 − 3 = 2; 7 − 4 = 3; 10 − 5 = 5; 9 − 2 = 7; 8 − 7 = 1; 9 − 6 = 3; 6 − 1 = 5; 10 − 2 = 8; 7 − 5 = 2; 5 − 1 = 4; 8 − 2 = 6; 8 − 0 = 8; 9 − 7 = 2; 8 − 5 = 3; 10 − 4 = 6; 10 − 3 = 7; 9 − 4 = 5; 8 − 1 = 7; 6 − 4 = 2; 6 − 3 = 3; 7 − 2 = 5; 9 − 0 = 9; 10 − 1 = 9

Page 307

2, 3, 2; 3, 2, 1

Pages 308–309

1. 9 − 4 = 5; 2. 8 − 1 = 7;
3. 10 − 3 = 7; 4. 8 − 6 = 2;
5. 7 − 2 = 5; 6. 8 − 4 = 4
7. 10 − 4 = 6; 8. 8 − 2 = 6;
9. 9 − 6 = 3

Scholastic Professional Books

Page 310

Page 311

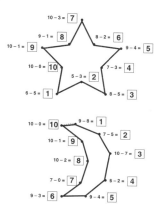

Page 312

4, 3, 2; 10, 1, 7; 6, 8, 5; The rabbit moved right to add. The rabbit moved left to subtract.

Page 313

Page 314

IT'S OUT OF THIS WORLD!

Page 315

A. 6 + 2 = 8; B. 3 + 1 = 4;
C. 6 − 4 = 2

Page 316

A. 6 + 4 = 10; B. 10 − 5 = 5; C. 9 − 2 = 7; D. 4 + 6 = 10; E. 7 + 2 = 9; F. 2 + 3 = 5; G. 5 + 3 = 8; H. 6 + 4 = 10; I. 8 − 7 = 1; J. 10 − 3 = 7

Page 317

A. 7 + 3 = 10; B. 7 − 4 = 3; C. 10 − 6 = 4; D. 8 − 2 = 6; E. 5 + 4 = 9

Page 318

Check child's coloring.
11 ways; 0 + 10 = 10, 1 + 9 = 10, 2 + 8 = 10, 3 + 7 = 10, 4 + 6 = 10, 5 + 5 = 10, 6 + 4 = 10, 7 + 3 = 10, 8 + 2 = 10, 9 + 1 = 10, 0 + 10 = 10

Page 319

7 leaps

Page 320
8 + 7 = 15; 3 + 7 = 10; 8 + 6 = 14;
9 + 9 = 18; 1 + 1 = 2; 5 + 2 = 7;
3 + 2 = 5; 9 + 2 = 11; 4 + 2 = 6;
1 + 4 = 5; 2 + 2 = 4; 7 + 4 = 11;
5 + 8 = 13; 6 + 2 = 8; 7 + 7 = 14;
5 + 5 = 10; 4 + 7 = 11; 3 + 3 = 6;
1 + 7 = 8; 3 + 8 = 11; 5 + 0 = 5;
9 + 6 = 15; 5 + 3 = 8; 2 + 5 = 7;
0 + 2 = 2; 3 + 1 = 4; 9 + 7 = 16;
7 + 5 = 12; 6 + 1 = 7; 9 + 8 = 17;
1 + 5 = 6; 6 + 6 = 12
Elephant

Page 321
Beans talk.
4 + 2 = 6; 7 + 7 = 14; 9 + 5 = 14
10 + 4 = 14; 4 + 8 = 12; 6 + 8 = 14
11 + 3 = 14; 14 + 0 = 14; 7 + 2 = 9
13 + 1 = 14; 5 + 8 = 13; 12 + 2 = 14
7 + 4 = 11; 5 + 9 = 14

Page 322
A.

2	4	6
3	1	4
5	5	10

B.

4	1	5
7	3	10
11	4	15

C.

6	7	13
2	1	3
8	8	16

D.

5	6	11
4	3	7
9	9	18

E.

2	6	8
5	0	5
7	6	13

F.

4	7	11
3	3	6
7	10	17

Page 323
8, 8; 4, 4; 6, 6; 8, 8; 1, 1; 3, 3; 9, 9;
2, 2; 5, 5; 7, 7; even

Page 324
7 + 7 = 14, 5 + 5 = 10, 8 + 8 = 16,
6 + 6 = 12; 9 + 9 = 18, 3 + 3 = 6,
2 + 2 = 4; 4 + 4 = 8

Page 325
A. 4; B. 6; C. 10; D. 9; E. 7; F. 2;
G. 5; H. 8; I. 3; J. 1; K. 5 – 2 = 3;
L. 9 – 3 = 6; M. 7 – 5 = 2;
N. 8 – 1 = 7; O. 12 – 6 = 6;
P. 16 – 8 = 8; Q. 14 – 5 = 9

Page 326
four, five; seven, eleven; nine, six;
ten, three; eight, two

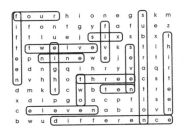

Page 327
7 + 2 = **9** – 4 = **5** – 3 = **2** + 9 = **11** +
5 = **16** – 8 = **8** + 4 = **12** + 6 = **18** – 9
= **9** + 1 = **10** + 4 = **14** – 8 = **6** + 2 =
8 + 3 = **11** – 3 = **8**; 12 – 3 = **9** – 6 =
3 + 2 = **5** + 9 = **14** – 6 = **8** + 7 = **15** –
6 = **9** + 3 = **12** – 2 = **10** + 7 = **17** + 1
= **18** – 11 = **7** – 5 = **2** + 13 = **15** – 7
= **8** + 3 = **11**; Color the bottom car
blue.

Page 328

3 peanuts

Page 329

3, 3; 7, 7; 9, 9; 5, 5; 8, 8

Page 330

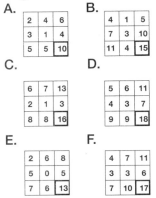

A. First flower should be circled.;
B. 8 + 9 = 17; C. 5 – 5 = 0;
D. 5 + 3 = 8; E. 5 – 3 = 2;
F. 9 + 5 = 14

Page 331
A. 13, 12, 13, 13; B. 12, 11, 11, 11;
C. 17, 15, 15, 17; D. 14, 14, 14, 16
Check child's coloring.

Page 332
–1; 12, 11, 10, 9, 8, 7
+2; 2, 4, 6, 8, 10, 12
+3; 3, 6, 9, 12, 15, 18
–2; 13, 11, 9, 7, 5, 3

Scholastic Professional Books

Page 333

2, 4, 2; 3, 5, 4; 6, 4, 10;
Answers will vary.

Page 334

5; 3 + 2 + 5 = 10; 4 + 5 + 7 = 16; 6; 7
+ 2 = 9; 6 − 2 = 4; 7 + 4 + 5 + 3 + 2
= 21; 1 + 7 + 6 + 3 + 2 = 19

Page 335

Page 336

Check child's coloring.; 14 days

Page 337

	17	36	84	
78	29	59	14	48
88	24	35	66	98
18	43	77	38	88
78	65	56	46	26
	99	57	87	

Page 338

93 + 6 = 99, 82 + 4 = 86, 14 + 5 =
19, 21 + 7 = 28, 53 + 6 = 59; 45 + 4
= 49, 73 + 3 = 76, 36 + 3 = 39, 61 +
5 = 66, 32 + 7 = 39; 4 + 7 + 5 + 3 +
6 = 25

Page 339

Page 340

Check child's coloring.

Page 341

A. 39 − 7 = 32; B. 54 − 1 = 53; C. 87
− 6 = 81;
D. 73 − 3 = 70; E. 25 − 4 = 21; F. 42
− 2 = 40;
G. 98 − 7 = 91; H. 66 − 5 = 61;
4, 7, 5

Page 342

42, 90, 76, 32, 82, 63, 81; 50, 35,
21, 21, 41, 90, 53; 30, 80, 20, 70,
60, 65, 74; The box with 53 should
be colored yellow. The box with 32
should be colored orange. The box
with 74 should be colored red.

Page 343

Check child's coloring.

Page 344

AT

12 + 13 = 25; 24 + 34 = 58;
22 + 21 = 43; 77 + 22 = 99;
35 + 43 = 78; 52 + 12 = 64
40 + 52 = 92; 11 + 31 = 42;
30 + 39 = 69; 46 + 52 = 98;
15 + 12 = 27; 10 + 71 = 81;
63 + 11 = 74; 13 + 80 = 93;
36 + 32 = 68; 30 + 10 = 40;
11 + 11 = 22; 15 + 4 = 19
20 + 21 = 41; 15 + 11 = 26;
22 + 33 = 55; 14 + 14 = 28;
13 + 16 = 29; 10 + 20 = 30;
14 + 25 = 39; 11 + 20 = 31;
15 + 21 = 36; 20 + 31 = 51;
36 + 52 = 88; 21 + 32 = 53;
10 + 50 = 60; 44 + 41 = 85;
24 + 43 = 67; 31 + 21 = 52;
13 + 82 = 95;

Page 345

32 + 24 = 56; 16 + 40 = 56;
54 + 14 = 68; 77 + 12 = 89;
34 + 34 = 68; 53 + 36 = 89;
26 + 63 = 89; 23 + 45 = 68;
35 + 62 = 97; 38 + 30 = 68;
22 + 67 = 89; 47 + 42 = 89

Page 346

HE WAS A CHICKEN.

13 + 11 = 24; 26 + 33 = 59;
16 + 31 = 47; 10 + 12 = 22;
64 + 24 = 88; 20 + 15 = 35;
71 + 12 = 83; 25 + 21 = 46;
51 + 10 = 61; 22 + 16 = 38;
22 + 10 = 32; 14 + 14 = 28;
20 + 10 = 30; 25 + 31 = 56;
21 + 3 = 24; 42 + 30 = 72;
13 + 43 = 56; 54 + 15 = 69;
21 + 61 = 82; 61 + 33 = 94;
10 + 30 = 40; 20 + 30 = 50;
16 + 32 = 48; 71 + 23 = 94;
70 + 20 = 90

Page 347

A BAT

5 – 2 = 3; 7 – 7 = 0; 18 – 9 = 9;
17 – 3 = 14; 15 – 4 = 11;
18 – 4 = 14; 12 – 3 = 9;
11 – 9 = 2; 16 – 9 = 7; 7 – 4 = 3;
10 – 8 = 2; 15 – 7 = 8; 9 – 2 = 7;
13 – 2 = 11; 12 – 2 = 10;
15 – 2 = 13; 9 – 6 = 3; 6 – 6 = 0;
9 – 7 = 2; 15 – 9 = 6; 16 – 8 = 8;
9 – 5 = 4; 9 – 1 = 8

Page 348

77 – 30 = 47; 76 – 62 = 14;
59 – 12 = 47; 85 – 52 = 33;
98 – 84 = 14; 87 – 40 = 47;
98 – 35 = 63; 58 – 11 = 47;
88 – 62 = 26; 77 – 14 = 63;
69 – 22 = 47; 38 – 12 = 26;
75 – 12 = 63; 97 – 71 = 26;
97 – 50 = 47; 98 – 51 = 47;
43 – 10 = 33; 87 – 73 = 14;
78 – 31 = 47; 97 – 64 = 33;
99 – 52 = 47

Page 349

1. 7 – 1 = 6; 2. 9 – 2 = 7;
3. 3 – 2 = 1; 4. 8 – 4 = 4,
5. 5 – 5 = 0; 6. 6 – 1 = 5;
7. 8 – 2 = 6

The phone number is 671-4056.

Page 350

27, 74, 41, 65; 27, 70, 42, 53; 15,
23, 11, 33; 20, 2, 15, 31; 22

Page 351

Answers will vary.

Page 352

34 + 13 = 47, 21 + 52 = 73, 47 + 10
= 57; 75 – 34 = 41, 62 – 21 = 41, 47
– 13 = 34

Page 353

A. Sunday; B. 89;
C. Monday; D. 24; E. 79; F. 22;
Sunday, Tuesday, Saturday

Page 354

34, 85, 26, 57; star; 71, 88, 42, 76,
85; light; 76, 63, 26, 85; heat; 71,
88, 13, 63; life

Page 355

Page 356

Answers
will vary.

MATH

Page 359

Check child's picture to make sure
each shape has the correct color:

6 = yellow;

7 = green;

8 = brown;

9 = red;

10 = green

Page 360

Answers will vary, but check to
make sure that child has supplied
correct numbers for each category.

Page 361

Check to make sure that child has
drawn lines from five different frogs
to the lily pads.

No; 2 frogs need lily pads

Page 362

1. Answers will vary.

2. Numbers will be colored in using an AB pattern of red and blue.

Page 363

Possible groups

Balls: soccer ball, basketball, rubber ball

Winter clothes: scarf, hat, boots

Art supplies: paint, paintbrush, crayon

Page 364

Check child's picture to make sure that each shape has the correct color:

one = green;

two = yellow;

three = red;

four = purple;

five = blue

Page 365

Yield sign: triangle, 3

Caution sign: diamond, 4

Speed-limit sign: rectangle, 4

Stop sign: octagon, 8

Page 366

Left birdhouse: cube, octagon, hexagon, rectangle, square, rectangle solid

Right birdhouse: cylinder, triangle, circle, rectangle

Page 367

Color the first butterfly, the second heart, the lightbulb, and the snowflake; drawings should show the other halves.

Page 368

1. 32, 42, 52, 62, 72, 82, 92

2. 70, 60, 50, 40, 30, 20, 10

3. 67, 57, 47, 37, 27, 17, 7

4. 44, 55, 66, 77, 88, 99

Page 369

A salamander

Page 370

Estimates will vary. 2, 4, 6, 8, 10, 12, 14, 16, 18, 20, 5, 10, 15, 20

Extra: No. Snowflakes would melt before you could count them.

Page 371

1	2	3	4	5	6	7	8	9	10
11	12	13	14	15	16	17	18	19	20
21	22	23	24	25	26	27	28	29	30
31	32	33	34	35	36	37	38	39	40
41	42	43	44	45	46	47	48	49	50
51	52	53	54	55	56	57	58	59	60
61	62	63	64	65	66	67	68	69	70
71	72	73	74	75	76	77	78	79	80
81	82	83	84	85	86	87	88	89	90
91	92	93	94	95	96	97	98	99	100

Answers will vary.

Page 372

4 + 4 = 8

5 + 5 = 10

6 + 6 = 12

7 + 7 = 14

8 + 8 = 16

Extra: 6, 8, 10, 12, 14, 16

Pattern: Count by 2s, even numbers, doubling

Page 373

Child's patterns and equations will vary.

Page 374

5; Answers will vary.

Page 375

Answers will vary.

Page 376

Answers will vary.

Page 377

15; 8

Page 378

Alex's coins: 5¢ + 25¢ + 10¢ = 60¢

Billy's coins: 10¢ + 10¢ + 10¢ + 10¢ + 10¢ + 5¢ + 5¢ + 1¢ + 1¢ + 1¢ = 63¢

63¢ > 60¢ Billy has more money.

Page 379

1¢: 10 coins for 10¢

5¢: 4 coins for 20¢

10¢: 2 coins for 20¢

25¢: 2 coins for 50¢

Page 380

Answers will vary.

Page 381

3 1/2 inches, 2 inches, 1 1/2 inches, 3 inches

Patty, Peter, Petunia, Paul

Page 382

pencil: 2

lunchbox: 1

crayon: 2

notebook: 1

Page 383

1 gallon = 4 quarts

1 quart = 2 pints

1 pint = 2 cups

1 cup = 12 tablespoons

1 tablespoon = 3 teaspoons

Page 384

1 + 2 + 1 + 2 = 6 inches

2 + 3 + 2 + 3 = 10 inches

2 + 5 + 2 + 5 = 14 inches

Page 385

book height: 2 centimeters

book width: 3 centimeters

straw: 6 centimeters

marker: 4 centimeters

5 cubes: 4 centimeters

10 cubes: 8 centimeters

shoe: 5 centimeters

hand: 3 centimeters

Page 386

Answers will vary. The following is a likely answer. Check children's graphs to make sure that they correspond to the boxes checked.

chicken: see, hear, smell, touch

sun: see

lemonade: see, touch, taste

flowers: see, smell, touch

drums: see, hear, touch

Page 387

Answers will vary.

Page 388

Page 389

Page 390

Sunny days: 12

Cloudy days: 8

Rainy days: 5

Snowy days: 6

Page 391

Color shapes 1, 2, 5, 6, 7, and 8.

Page 392

1/5 of the circle, 4/5 of the rectangle, 3 ants, 2 spiders, 0 bees, 5 worms

Page 393

1/8 of the circle, 6/8 of the square, 4 suns, 8 stars,

2 moons, 3 planets

Page 394

Page 395

Page 396

Page 397

Answers will vary.